# Journey to Enya

*a story about managing teams*

Nick Leja

# Dedication


To us.

# Acknowledgements

Thank you to the following friends and family for proofreading my initial manuscript and providing valuable feedback: Noah Leja, Nick Bemiss, Maria Viviano-Jurinic, Andy Weir, Alyson Weir, Max Jarzeboski, Jared Fisher, Leo Glenn Manlongat, Kim Rooker, Sue Leja-Mac, and Brionna Hayes. A special thanks to Kelly Viviano for editing my initial manuscript, providing numerous pointers in helping me spread the word, and for constantly cheering me on whenever I felt down. Another special thanks to Lisa Arnold for dramatically helping me with vivid descriptions and fun word choices that helped to bring my characters and scenes to life.

Also – thank you to my dad for continuously pushing me to get back into writing, my mom for helping me see there's more to life than business, and my brother for always being there for me, especially when my cards are down.

Any wisdom you find in these pages came from reading other great authors or personal experiences with my team members, friends, and family. None of this would be possible without them.

# 1

"She has two, maybe three months at the most."

My vision blurred. The sounds in the hallway drifted away, becoming muffled as if the words had tugged me underwater. My pulse overshadowed all other noises, becoming the loudest thing I could hear, the only thing I could feel.

I looked from the doctor down to my daughter. She appeared so peaceful, her tiny eyes closed, her golden fur clean and brushed, the white linen sheet pulled up to her shoulders. A young mouse with her whole life ahead of her. She didn't deserve to be in a coma like this. She was too young.

"Martin," the doctor said, her voice distant yet grabbing me and pulling me back.

My gaze remained on Ella. My throat felt raw, stinging with a sharp pain every time I swallowed.

"Martin," the doctor's voice came through again, her white paw slipping into view as it supportively held my arm.

"How?" I managed to say. "How is this possible?"

"I'm so sorry." Doctor Farah's voice sounded a little closer. "She has a very rare disease called *cornomiasa*. I've only seen it a handful of times.

I can't imagine—"

"There has to be something you can do," I interrupted, my gaze snapping from my daughter up to the doctor's eyes.

Doctor Farah's beady eyes closed and her head dropped. "I can't. All our herbs and salves can provide comfort, but we don't have anything that can—"

"What other options are there?" I asked. "Someone must have something. I'll take her anywhere. I'll do anything."

"No one has anything," she continued. "There is only one cure that we know of."

My senses sharpened back into focus. I could suddenly hear and see everything, every detail. There was hope.

"There's an herb called *chai thistle*."

"Great," I said immediately. "Where can I find it?"

The doctor took a deep breath. "It's not that easy. Chai thistle has only been found on the northern island of Enya. Once picked, the herb dies within three to four weeks, so no shop would have any. You'd have to go there yourself to get it."

This decision required no thought.

"I'll do it," I said, ready to do anything to save Ella. "How do I find this island?"

"Some shopkeepers sell maps to the island, but the journey won't be easy. You must travel by sea. As you know, wind only blows to the south, so you'll need a galley ship to move against it. My brother is a fishermouse, and according to the stories from other captains, it's about a five-week journey from here to Enya with a full crew. The ship and crew will be expensive."

"Five weeks?" I said. "You said the herb only lasts for three weeks. I wouldn't make it back in time."

"On the way back," she said, "you'll be able to use the sails to move at least twice as fast. That being said, it's still a very narrow window, so you'll need a good crew."

"What if we brought Ella with us?"

"She's dependent on the care we provide here, which would be impossible to offer at sea."

"Okay," I said, disappointed. "How much chai thistle do I need?"

"Ten ounces will be plenty."

The doctor seemed like she was about to say something but decided against it. We both gazed at each other for a few seconds as I went through everything she had said like a bird reviewing his notes before his first flight.

I had no time to waste. I needed to go.

I approached my daughter and knelt by her bed. Taking her tiny paw in my hand, I massaged it gently, and then squeezed her paw and rested it against my cheek.

She felt warm. So warm.

"Don't worry, Ella. I'll be back soon. I promise. Just rest. All you have to do now is rest."

After a minute of holding her close and feeling the weakening heartbeat in her wrist, I tucked her paw back under the sheet, stood up, and headed for the exit.

"Martin," the doctor said as I opened the wooden door.

One paw on the doorknob, I turned around to face her. "Yes?"

"The journey to Enya is very dangerous. Dozens of crews have tried to make the voyage, hundreds of merchants have tried to gather chai thistle for profit, and very few have ever made it back alive. Despite how valuable it is, no merchant even tries anymore. Those who have made it back said nature doesn't want critters that far north. There's something out there. Something dangerous."

Maybe I should've taken the doctor's words more seriously. Maybe I should've asked more questions and gathered as much information as I could to prepare for the journey.

But I didn't.

Instead, I simply nodded and left the room.

# 2

"Thank you," I said, dropping three pieces of copper on the desk. I took the rolled parchment from the shopkeeper in one hand, its protective tube in the other, and walked back out onto the cobblestoned streets of Cherrystone.

A few critters bustled about the streets, mainly mice with a few badgers and moles sprinkled throughout. Cherrystone wasn't exactly a tourist town, so everyone walked with a sense of purpose, no lost visitors asking for directions or outsiders interrupting foot traffic to gawk at a landmark.

Once outside, I set the tube against the wall and unrolled the parchment to look at the map. The sea engulfed the entire west side of the map, with land nudging outward from the east. The main continent began at the lower center of the map but tapered to the right as it sprawled northward with seven little fishing villages dotting the coast.

Then, there it was, towards the top left: Enya, a lone island surrounded by the icy sea. Scribbled beneath the island were the words "Beware of Sibyl." What did that mean?

I almost stepped back into the shop to ask the shopkeeper, but then remembered he simply sold various goods. He didn't make them. Besides, my crew was waiting for me, so I needed to go.

Satisfied with the map, I rolled it up, slipped it into the tube, and fastened the tube behind my back, its thin leather strap stretching diagonally across my chest.

Securing the map completed my checklist, so I started walking down the path to the docks.

The massive loan secured by my shelter, brother, and parents weighed heavily on my mind. Even with it, I barely had enough money to rent a ship and hire a crew. Doctor Farah hadn't been kidding when she'd warned of this trip's danger, or at least the perception of it. Trying to rent a ship from a critter once they knew my destination was like trying to crack open a coconut with a twig.

Same for the crew. Every critter knew how dangerous the journey was, so every critter demanded premium pay.

Whatever. It was worth it. There was no price I wouldn't pay to save Ella.

At the next intersection, I turned right where the street began to ramp down towards the sea.

Although I tried to portray confidence to the lenders and shopkeepers, self-doubts and fears flooded my mind whenever I had a moment to think. I'd never managed critters before. As a weaver, my team consisted of one mouse: myself. Just me and my needles and my threads.

My father had once owned a shop that sold nuts and seeds. He absolutely loved nuts and seeds to the point where he took it a little too far. Once, we were going for a hike up Mount Hilltop, and my dad literally ran me over when he saw a new type of nut by the cliff. It wasn't until a few moments later that he realized he'd nearly knocked me off the edge.

But when he opened his own shop, he was always so stressed. Running a shop, he used to say, is all about the team. Eighty percent of his time went to managing the critters working for him, trying to work with and motivate critters with vastly different personalities, preferences, and skillsets. Most of the remaining time was spent on all the paperwork, which left very little time for him to explore his true passion: nuts and seeds.

Now, for the first time in my life, I had to lead a team. Not just a few critters selling stuff, but a full crew sailing through some of the most dangerous waters known to mammals. I needed to learn a lot to—

"Imagine leading a crew with *thiiis!*"

I jumped back in shock as a shrew popped up in front of me, holding a round monocle about three whiskers' width from my face.

"Whoa!" I said, stopping dead in my tracks and then retreating a couple of paces.

"Well?" the shrew asked as he followed me, denying me any extra breathing room.

This shrew looked pretty similar to a mouse, only he had a long, pointed snout and tiny eyes. Dark brown fur ran along his top and sides, but his underside fur was a light grey, presenting quite the contrast. He wore a thick coat that looked too warm for this weather. Whatever he kept in his cloak jingled and clinked with his every movement.

"Umm... no thanks," I said. "I can see just fine."

"Silly mouse," he said as he lowered the monocle towards my paws, encouraging me to try it. "This isn't for seeing." He paused. "It's for *seeing.*"

*What an odd fellow.* I took the monocle from him and tried it on. I expected to see nothing, so the greenish tint that covered the shrew's fur when viewed through the monocle surprised me. However, when I looked around at other critters nearby, they all looked normal. It was probably some trick. Maybe the shrew put on some fragrance or something and this monocle had a lens that visualized the aroma with color. Interesting for sure, but I wasn't in the mood for magic tricks.

I took it off and tried handing it back, but his paw pressed against mine in a stopping gesture.

"I can tell yer on a voyage," the shrew said, indicating the tube strapped to my back. "You'll be leading a crew, won't ya?"

He invited an awkward silence to join our conversation until I eventually nodded.

"This monocle was enchanted by a snow owl. It allows you to see the work ethic of each member of yer team," he explained. "Green is good, yellow is so-so, and red is no-no."

If this monocle was truly enchanted by an owl as this shifty vendor proclaimed, it would be a very precious artifact indeed. However, I'd been fooled by such claims in the past, and I wasn't in the mood.

"No thank you," I said and walked past the shrew, continuing towards the docks.

Unfortunately, the shrew's clanking and clacking merged with my shadow and followed.

"If it works, then would you want it?" he asked.

"Sure," I said without looking back or stopping.

"When we get to the docks, I'll prove it to you."

He wanted to follow me all the way to the docks. Oh joy.

Between all his gadgets banging against one another and him trying to sell me everything he could think of, silence remained a distant fantasy the entire trip down to the marina.

When we arrived, I paused to take in the view. Ships of all sizes huddled throughout the bay, some at port, others anchored in the water, and still others sailing into the rising sun. Mist from the crashing waves wafted from sea to land, cooling the air and then allowing the sunlight to warm it back up. The waves slapping against the docks and the wood creaking from critters bustling about generated a soothing ambiance. Even my new friend took a moment to take it all in without talking. Silence at last scored a victory, however brief.

Despite the beautiful sights, it was time to go. Noticing a dockhand nearby, I approached her and showed her the papers with my ship's information.

"This way," she said, and I followed her down the wooden docks for what seemed like forever. At one point, I had to practically backflip to get out of the way of a few mice pushing a cart full of lumber down the narrow walkway. Environmental awareness didn't seem to be a strong suit of these dock-dwellers.

"There she is," my escort said, motioning leftwards towards a small galley ship docked at the edge of a wooden path. The ship was a lot smaller than I expected. Six oars poked out of each side and rested a few inches above the water. Three round masts stretched up towards the sky with sails furled on top. The deck itself remained rather bare save for a few barrels of supplies. Bright white letters painted on the back spelled the ship's name: *Skimmer*.

"And there's yer crew," she said pointing to the right.

To the side was a small grub outpost, just barely big enough for one or two workers inside, and a tiny adjacent roped-in area speckled with small barrels and wooden blocks. The seating looked just comfortable enough to convince critters to stop by but not lounge-worthy enough to encourage them to stay past their meal.

Sitting on those uncomfortable barrels and blocks and crowding the spaces between were my crew: twenty-one of them. They were all mice, some large, some small, but all physically fit to man an oar for several hours per day. Or so they claimed.

None of the crew seemed to notice me except for one mouse off to the side resting against a wooden post on the perimeter of the area. She was a fierce-looking mouse, tall with bright white and gray fur. As soon as I arrived, she shot me a stare that could shatter stone, almost as if saying: *I know you have zero qualifications to lead this crew.* Retreating to my weaving shop never seemed more appealing.

My new vendor friend's elbow pressed into my side a couple times as he leaned closer. "Go ahead, mate," he said in a quiet voice, presenting the monocle once more. "Give 'er a try."

Eager to tell the shrew I wasn't interested and shoo him away, I slipped the monocle over my right eye.

Wow. He wasn't pulling my tail after all. Looking through the monocle, each of my crew members had a faint tint: green, yellow, and red, roughly evenly distributed. Well, exactly evenly distributed: seven of each color. The fierce-looking mouse was green, a label for *good* according to the vendor. Hopefully seeing me looking at everyone with a monocle didn't diminish what little confidence she may have had in me.

Several moments passed while I tried to understand how the monocle worked. Owls were mystical creatures who frequently enchanted artifacts, but this was the first one I'd experienced firsthand.

After a while, I took the monocle off and held it in my paw, examining it. "How does it work?"

"I told you," the shrew said. "It detects the work ethic of the critter yer viewing and then tints that critter's fur so you can see it."

"When I tried it on earlier in town, you were the only critter with color. Why wasn't anyone else colored?"

"The monocle only works on critters who are in their work environment," the vendor explained. "Most critters don't have absolute good or bad work ethics; it changes based on the work they're performing. Some critters love gardening and would show green while gardening, but those same critters could show red when working as a cook."

"Hmm..." I said, thinking. "So what should I do with critters who are red?"

The shrew gripped his belly and released an exaggerated laugh.

"That's for you to figure out, lad. I just sell stuff."

I looked at the monocle resting in my paw. Although I didn't quite know what I would do with the information, part of me felt like it would prove useful. Somehow.

"How much?" I asked, bracing for impact. There was no way this would be cheap.

"Five silver," the shrew said quickly, sounding relieved I'd finally asked.

That made the decision easy. I moved to hand it back. "I can't afford it, I'm sorry."

"Well, let's hold on there for a moment, friend," he said, without moving to take back the monocle. "Where ya headin'?"

"Enya."

"So yer sailing north. Not many ships sail that way." The shrew scratched his narrow, scruffy chin while he spoke, and then, apparently having come to decision, he dropped his hand back to his side and looked at me. "Tell ya what. I don't get a chance to go north very often. I'm sure there are plenty of uncommon wares I can find to bring back and sell. Let me hitch a ride on yer vessel up to Nibbletown. Then I'll give you this monocle free of charge. How's that for a deal?"

It wouldn't cost me much other than some food and a little extra weight aboard. Nibbletown was only two villages away, so he'd be gone before the currents picked up.

"Deal."

"Great!" the shrew said and immediately hustled towards the ship. "Oh!" he stopped a few paces later and turned around. "Name's Rico."

"Martin."

Rico nodded and gave an extravagant bow. "A pleasure." And then he hurried aboard the *Skimmer*.

# 3

When I turned back to my crew, an older mouse was approaching me. His fur had greyed with age with some patches turning white. A wooden peg replaced the bottom half of his right leg, so he held a weathered cane and used it for balance as he walked. Was he physically capable of this voyage?

"You must be Martin," he said when he got close, his voice oddly soothing.

"Yes, and you are?"

"Leo," he said with a warm smile. "It's a pleasure meeting you."

"Oh, so you're my first mate," I said, visualizing the paperwork I received earlier.

"Aye aye, Cap'n," he said in a playfully formal voice.

I laughed. "You can just call me Martin."

"Sounds good, Martin. You ready for this?"

I remembered my dad telling me the importance of sounding confident when leading. Although every part of my mind was saying no, I managed to squeak out the most confident *yes* I could muster.

Leo gave me a comforting look. Part of him likely knew the real answer, but he let me save face and continued.

"I've been on a lot of voyages," he said. "Never to Enya, of course. She's one of the last destinations on my list before I retire from the sea-faring life."

I couldn't help but glance down at his peg leg again, still wondering if he was suited for this voyage.

"Pirates," he said, lifting his peg leg and turning it this way and that to show it off. "Got hit with an arrow in my back paw during a voyage. It got infected, and we didn't have the proper herbs to heal it. So now I have one less paw to clean!" He spoke with an unusual amount of optimism, which I admired.

"Are you going to be okay on this voyage?" I asked.

"I'll be fine," he said without hesitation. "You don't need feet to row an oar."

Fair point.

He brought his peg leg back to the dock and tapped it twice. "Okay Martin, we should get going. It's two full days until we reach the first port town of Dormeadow. We want to ensure we secure a dock early so we don't get stuck at sea."

I nodded. "Alright, I'll see you aboard."

Leo smiled. "See you aboard."

Leo walked past me, and I listened to the rhythm of the floorboards squeaking under his paw and the double thud of his peg leg and cane. Squeak. *Thud-thud.* Squeak. *Thud-thud.* His presence softened my thoughts and concerns, allowing me to loosen up and relax a bit.

After seeing my conversation with Leo end, the rest of the critters finished nibbling their food and swallowing their cordials, and then they headed my way.

"Hi!" a younger female mouse said as she approached. She had a beautiful violet patch of fur on the back of her head and neck. "I'm Kia! Nice to meet you, Martin!"

It was weird having everyone know my name without my knowing theirs.

"Nice to meet you, Kia," I said with a smile.

"It's my absolute dream to be a captain one day. If there's ever anything I can do to help, please let me know!"

She probably already had more qualifications to be captain than I.

"Of course, Kia."

"See you aboard!"

Next up was another female mouse with darker fur, almost black.

"Name's Lilly," she said.

"Nice to meet you."

"Just so you know," she said, glancing back over her shoulder to make sure no one could hear before putting her face so close to my ear that her whiskers tickled my cheek, "One of the crew, Collin, has been complaining nonstop. He's frustrated with the crew, especially that your first mate has a peg leg. He's asking everyone how much they're getting paid and encouraging us to ask for more."

My heart grew heavier as she spoke. I hadn't even set foot on the ship, and issues with my team had already begun sprouting up.

"Personally," she continued. "I think he should go. He's a bad piece of cheese, let me tell you. Although he does bring up some good points. For one, how much experience *do* you have leading a crew?"

Fortunately, she didn't give me a chance to answer. "Second, is pay negotiable? I know we haven't sailed yet and there's a lot of unknowns, but if we work harder, do we get paid more? Or do we get the same no matter how hard we work? Third—"

"Alright, Lilly," came a gruff voice from the mouse behind her. "Let's keep moving. He doesn't have time for this right now. You can talk his ear off once we depart."

"Fine, fine," Lilly said and rushed past me towards the ship.

"Hi," the male mouse behind her said, stepping up. "My name's Walter. I know you won't remember half of what we say here, so I'll get to know you aboard the *Skimmer*. Savvy?"

I nodded, starting to feel a little overwhelmed with all the different personalities.

The rest of the crew continued moving past in a line. Most of them just introduced themselves with their name and a quick pleasantry, some went into more detail, and some of the shyer critters just smiled and nodded. That was more my speed: smiling and nodding. Too much was going on for me to have a meaningful conversation with everyone.

Relief washed over me when I realized only one mouse remained, but that relief turned to dread when I saw it was the fierce-looking mouse from earlier. Despite her intense face, her fur was beautiful, flowing patterns of vivid greys and whites weaving around her body. I didn't quite know what to make of her. I hoped she would simply nod and walk past, but she stopped. No one remained behind her to urge her along. This would be interesting.

"H-hello," I said. "My name's Martin, and you are?"

"Artemis," she said, her eyes judging every part of me like I was the most unimpressive mouse she'd ever met. "How many voyages have you been on?"

"This would be my first."

"Your first?"

"Yes."

"Why are you doing this?"

I explained about my daughter and my mission. She seemed indifferent, my words deflecting off her like dandelion seeds against steel.

"Leo's a great first mate," she said. "He should be captain instead of you."

Harsh. But true.

"Let me give you a word of advice," she continued. "Don't try to please everyone. That's one of the worst traits of a captain."

I nodded. "No, of course. Makes sense."

"The pay for this job is decent, but it's not great. If you don't have what it takes, I'm gone."

I didn't really know what type of response to give, but apparently, she didn't need one. After burning my soul for a few more seconds with her gaze, she walked past me to board the ship.

Finally, the introductions were over. I breathed a sigh of relief. It was times like these I really wished I was an extrovert. I had always taken a lot more comfort in quietly observing rather than being in the spotlight. Every critter seemed so confident with themselves and what they were doing. Was I the only one winging it out here?

"Another ship's waiting to dock," the dockhand mouse who showed me to my ship said. I had completely forgotten she was still there.

I smiled and nodded to her. "Alright, we'll head out." I'm sure *head out* wasn't the proper terminology. I probably should've said *set sail* or something. Either way, she nodded and walked away.

I approached the ship, and when I at last reached the gangway, I turned, pausing to view the ship in its entirety. Nobody aboard paid me any notice, each of them too busy laughing, talking, and bustling about in preparation for the voyage.

This was it. I allowed myself a moment to close my eyes and think of my daughter.

*Ella, just hold on. I don't know how to lead a crew, and I don't know what lies ahead. But I do know I won't fail. I can't. There is no going back. I will figure this out. I will find a way back to you. In two months' time, we'll be sitting around a fire, sipping pear cordials, laughing about all the stories from this journey. You'll see.*

*Just hold on.*

I walked up the gangway, letting my paw glide over the smooth deck railing when I reached the top. I took one last breath, steadying myself for what was ahead. There was no turning back.

Then, with loving thoughts of Ella pushing me forward, I stepped aboard.

# 4

I stood at the front of the ship (which Leo kept reminding me is called the *bow*) and watched it effortlessly cut through the water as it glided forward.

A few hours had passed since we left Cherrystone, and the last bit of land was just starting to fade behind us.

So far, things had been going pretty well. Crew morale seemed positive. Everyone's work ethic seemed good. No issues, though Leo deserved most of the credit. I didn't know what I would've done without him. Artemis surely would've thrown me overboard by now if not for him.

In the captain's quarters, Leo shared with me his suggestions for structuring the shifts. We had twenty-one crew members. During the twelve hours of daytime, ten critters would row (five per side), one would serve as the Officer of the Watch overseeing them, three would focus on fishing, two on cooking, and five resting. Every three hours, they would rotate. Ideally, we would've had twenty-three crew members to make use of six oars per side instead of five, but I couldn't afford that many crew.

During the nighttime shift, we would have only three rowers per side, and they would switch every six hours, mainly to keep the *Skimmer* from receding and drifting off track.

This schedule prevented anyone from getting overly fatigued and provided enough variety and rest for the crew. Everyone seemed "on board" with it.

"Imagine protecting your hands with *thiiis*," I heard Rico say to one of the mice rowing an oar.

I looked over to see Rico holding a small pair of leather gloves in front of an exhausted-looking mouse named Melvin. Although the gloves would be fairly useful, the way Rico spoke made any critter initially want to say *no*. He clearly used his little phrase over and over, and as most signatures look less like handwriting over time, his tone during his *imagine* line sounded unnatural, like a used wagon salesman.

Melvin took the opportunity to rest and examine the gloves but was immediately interrupted when Kia sprung up beside him.

"Not now, fellas!" she said in a chipper, yet stern, tone. She was currently the Officer of the Watch. "Only twenty minutes time until we rotate. I need all me oars critters moving full speed ahead."

"Can't the poor guy try them on?" Rico asked.

"Nope, nope!" Kia said. "Twenty minutes!" Kia turned around to face the rest of the critters. "Keep it up, my furry little navigators of the sea! Our shift is nearly complete. I'll be rowing after ye lot, so give me a pace that's tough to beat!"

Kia made her way down the deck, giving the critters encouragement when needed. She was strict, but she had a charming charisma about her, one that inspired her crew to work harder.

Rico looked at me for a second as if asking if I would override her. I shook my head; he took the hint and meandered elsewhere.

"Captain," a deep voice I recognized as Walter's reached my ears.

I turned to face him approaching me. "Call me Martin."

"Captain," he continued. So much for listening. "Can I have a word with you?"

"Sure," I said, waiting for him to speak.

Walter's eyes scanned around. "Somewhere more private?"

"How about my quarters?" I offered.

"Perfect."

We walked down the deck towards the back of the ship (*aft*, as Leo would remind me), climbed down the stairs leading below the quarter-deck, and entered my cabin.

My cabin was small but cozy. It smelled of fresh cedar, with a simple bed to the left, a desk in back under a curved window, and a small cabinet to the right. A lantern hung from the ceiling, but the sunlight coming in through the window provided plenty of light.

I sat at my desk, and Walter sat opposite of me.

"What's going on?" I asked.

"I have some concerns."

"Such as?"

"Leo's schedule is too strict. It doesn't give critters enough rest."

"We haven't even gone through a full rotation yet."

"I know, but critters have already started commenting on it."

"Like who?"

Walter paused for a second, thinking, scratching the dark brown fur on his face. "Just a few of the crew," he said dismissively.

21

"Okay… Do you have any suggestions?"

"Yes," he said, returning his hand to his lap. "We should have more breaks."

"Will all the work still get done, and will we stay on schedule?"

Again, Walter hesitated. I noticed the monocle on my desk to the side. Part of me wanted to grab it to see Walter's color, but it would be a bit awkward if I did it just then.

"I'm sure we will," he said with forced confidence.

"What did Leo say when you brought this up?"

"I didn't."

"You didn't talk to him first?"

"No."

"Why not?"

Irritation sliced through Walter's voice. "A lot of the crew are afraid to approach Leo."

"Who's afraid?" I asked.

"Just some of the crew."

Why was he being so vague with everything? How could I help if I didn't know the details?

"I know, but who?"

Walter fidgeted around in his chair and leaned a little closer. "The crew has started coming to me in confidence to share these concerns. They want to remain anonymous. I'm more of a spokesmouse for them. What you need to know is that they feel Leo's schedule is too strict, and no one feels comfortable approaching him."

We'd gone from a few of the crew being afraid of Leo to everyone.

The more Walter spoke, the harder it was for me to believe him.

But what should I do? I had my doubts with what he was saying, but this was also the first time I'd led a team. Maybe he was right. Maybe I should've been thanking him for confiding in me.

Every interaction I'd had with Leo had been great (which, to be fair, had only been a couple). Perhaps Leo acted differently around me than with everyone else?

How could I validate Walter's concerns if I didn't know their origins? Would it be best to approach the entire crew, asking each mouse if they thought the schedule is too strict? Wouldn't they all just say yes to get more breaks? Or would they consider the work involved to reach Enya in time?

Ahh, my mind was doing its thing again where it obsessed over concerns. I needed to focus and problem-solve.

"Captain?" Walter said.

"Yes?"

"You got quiet."

"I was thinking."

"So, what are you going to do?"

"What do you suggest?"

"I told you, I think you should change the schedule to give everyone more breaks."

My tail flicked back and forth nervously under pressure to make a decision. I couldn't agree with him right now, not without talking to Leo first.

"Let me talk it over with Leo," I said.

"When will you talk with him?" Walter pressed.

"Today."

"When?"

"As soon as I get the chance. Please, give me some time to handle this."

Walter's nose twitched a couple times, clearly not happy I didn't simply agree with him. "Okay," he said. "Just don't wait too long. I wouldn't want the crew getting too frustrated."

"I'm on it," I assured him.

"Okay," he said and stood up. He looked around the room. "These are pretty nice personal quarters you have here."

I didn't really know how to respond to that, and with my mind spinning about how to bring this up to Leo, I remained quiet.

After scanning my room a few more seconds, Walter looked at me and clapped his paws together. The sound made me jump. "Alright, I'm heading back on deck. Talk to you soon, captain."

Walter turned around and walked towards the door. Before he left, I quietly grabbed the monocle, slipped it over my right eye, and looked to see the color of Walter's fur under the magical lens.

Red.

# 5

After talking with Walter, I needed some fresh air. Before I left my cabin, I put the monocle in the breast pocket of my tunic.

The sunlight felt good on my face and whiskers. I closed my eyes for a moment to enjoy it, and then I walked up the quarterdeck to the ship's steering wheel (the helm). Alyssa, a taller mouse with light blue fur, was currently manning it.

"How's everything going?" I asked.

"Ahh, it's a beautiful day to be at sea, Cap'n!"

"Where's Leo?" I asked.

"He's talking with some of the crew below deck. He asked me to fill in for a bit."

"Gotcha." With Leo preoccupied, I decided to take this time to get to know Alyssa better. "So how many voyages have you been on?"

"This would be my fifth!" she said with excitement.

"That's really cool. You seem to have a knack for it."

"Thank you," she said.

"How's the crew doing?"

"Hmm…." She gave herself a few seconds to think. "So far so good. Many critters are pulling their weight, though some aren't. For instance," she stepped closer to me and pointed towards one of the mice manning an oar. "His name is Oscar. He's got the determination of a squirrel, rowing his oar twice as fast as you'd think given his size."

She turned and pointed to a mouse on the opposite side of the deck. "Him, on the other hand, that's Collin. I've had to tell him probably four times in the past hour to keep rowing. Okay, maybe that's a slight exaggeration, but my point is we'd probably be better off without him. Not only is he hardly rowing, but he's distracting the rest."

Looking at the crew and comparing Oscar to Collin, Alyssa's observation proved spot on. Collin clearly wasn't enjoying himself and moved at a fraction of the speed of everyone else. If I was Oscar, I'd be frustrated knowing how hard I rowed compared to Collin who barely put in any effort.

I grabbed the monocle from my pocket and slipped it over my eye. Sure enough, Oscar's fur glowed green and Collin's red.

"Have you spoken with Collin about this?"

"No," Alyssa said and gave a nervous laugh. "I'm great at sailing and navigating, but I'm not the best at critiquing critters." She reminded me of my father recalling his woes running the nuts and seed shop.

"No worries," I said. Looking through the monocle at the crew, I noticed a strong connection between the color of their fur and how quickly and energetically they rowed. The green mice seemed to be enjoying themselves, rowing more or less in sync. If one started rowing a little faster, the others would match them.

The yellow mice rowed at a steady pace. They didn't pay too much attention to others around them, and they didn't seem to have much urgency, but they kept on track.

The red mice, however, were a problem. They seemed bored or frustrated, scanning for something else to focus on or something to talk about: any excuse to take a break from work.

If every mouse rowed like the green mice, we would probably be sailing at triple the speed. Maybe this journey would be four weeks instead of five. Or maybe Doctor Farah's five-week estimate assumed the entire crew worked as well as the green-tinted mice. Maybe with this crew this journey would take eight weeks. Maybe longer.

Ella didn't have that much time.

I took off the monocle, slipped it back in my pocket, and rubbed my temples, trying to calm my thinking.

After a few seconds, Leo's peg leg hit the deck nearby, causing me to open my eyes and smile as he surfaced from below and approached us at the helm.

"Hey there Martin," he said to me. "How's your first day at sea treating you?"

"Good," I said. Despite my conversation with Walter, being secluded from everything happening on land felt refreshing, like we were in our own little world, free from the mundaneness of everyday life. This voyage also provided a sense of adventure, something I lacked from spending all my time weaving. I shouldn't have waited so long to do something like this.

The only things dragging me down were Walter's concerns, which I wanted to address.

"Leo, can I talk with you for a minute in my cabin?"

"I'd love to, but I'm next up on the rowing team." He looked at

Alyssa. "It's nearly time to switch, yeah?"

She retrieved a circular watch from her pocket, looked at it for a second, then nodded and put it away. "Aye, about three minutes time."

Leo looked back at me. "How about after my go at the oars? Max and I need to show these youngsters how it's done, right mate?"

My focus on my conversation with Leo had prevented me from noticing the bulky mouse beside him. He had black fur, a dark grey belly, and every muscle in his body rippled with definition. I remembered reading in his file that he had worked as a blacksmith for several years. He joined this voyage to collect rare metals and minerals from the northern regions to bring back to his shop.

Max gave a deep, bellowed laugh. "Right you are. Though I'm not so sure." He pointed to Oscar and Kia, two of the mice rowing the fastest. "Those two may give us a scurry for our copper."

"I agree," Leo said, turning to watch them. "I'm surprised at how fast they row given their size."

"I'm telling you, it's all mindset," Max said.

"Very true." Leo turned back to me. "Would it be alright if we talked after my rowing shift?"

I nodded. "Yes, absolutely. No rush."

"Great!" Leo said as he faced Max again. "Ready, friend?"

"Aye, aye."

The two of them walked down to the rowing critters to relieve them a couple minutes early. Shortly after, the rest of the new rowing team surfaced from below deck, relieved their fellow crewmates, and began rowing.

The former rowers stood up, stretched, flicked their tails back and forth to loosen up, and then scattered about for their next shift: fishing, cooking, or resting.

I spent the next few hours roaming the ship, getting to know the crew better. Fortunately, as an introvert, while I didn't enjoy being in the spotlight, I enjoyed learning about various critters and their stories, challenges they'd faced, goals, and so on. The variety of stories and personalities fascinated me. Most critters loved talking about themselves, so our conversations were easy and pleasant.

Some mice, like Alex, offered interesting and engaging conversation. A smaller mouse with reddish-brown fur, Alex shared his desire to be a chef. His intense excitement for us incorporating fishing and cooking shifts into our rotation made me laugh. He promised to serve me some of the best fish of my life during the voyage. No complaints here.

Others, like Lilly, started to give me a headache. Every time I bumped into her, Lilly would go on and on about who she felt worked hard, who didn't, who complained a lot, who didn't, and her thoughts on practically every mouse on board. To be fair, she did give me a heads up about Collin, so her comments didn't necessarily lack validity. They were just overwhelming. It felt impossible to wrap my head around all these problems, let alone try to solve them. Though maybe a good leader *could* process everything at once. Maybe a good leader *preferred* conversations like those instead of ones revolving around food.

By the time I finished mingling with the crew, the sun had taken on a crimson glow as it began its descent into the sea. Leaning against the rail, I watched the scarlet sunrays reflecting off the water, giving it the appearance of fresh cranberry juice. Other than another ship in the distance, water surrounded us as far as the eye could see. I enjoyed listening to the slight squeaking of the ship and the splashing of oars dipping into the water. It sounded like forward progress.

Most of my life had been very structured with hardly any surprises. I'd always felt safe, always secure, and always somewhat bored. I wished the context of this adventure was more positive, though I couldn't help but at least somewhat enjoy the thrill of it. Of course, this was only day one. We'd see how I was feeling towards the end.

With the sun halfway tucked into the horizon, I made my way back to my cabin and lit the lantern hanging from the ceiling to illuminate the room before the sunlight completely vanished. I also lit a couple candles on my desk so I could take notes if needed. After preparing some parchment, my quill, and ink on the desk, I sat down and gazed out the window.

As usual, the double-thumping of Leo's peg leg and cane betrayed his approach, allowing me to open the door just as he was about to knock.

"Good evening," he said with his usual smile.

"Thanks for coming, Leo. Please, have a seat." I pulled out the chair by the desk for him and then sat in mine.

He leaned his walking stick against the desk and then sat down. "What can I help you with?"

No wasting time on pleasantries. I appreciated him.

"Walter came to me today." I paused, seeing if he had any reaction to Walter's name. He didn't, so I continued. "He indicated several of the crew thought your work sch—*our* work schedule is too strict. He said the crew needed more time for rest."

"I see," Leo said. "What crew members had this issue?"

"He wouldn't say. He claimed they wanted to remain confidential."

"Of course," Leo said with a smile. "How many critters feel this way?"

"Well, first he said a few, and then it sounded like the entire crew."

"Does Walter himself feel this way?"

"I didn't ask specifically, but it sounded like he was just the messenger."

"Okay. What suggestions did he give for changing the schedule?"

"He didn't give any."

"Ah," Leo said. He remained quiet, taking slow, gentle breaths. Obviously, there was no way of knowing for sure, but it seemed like he wasn't thinking anything. Just waiting.

"What are your thoughts?" I asked after a while.

"What do *you* think?" he asked back.

My tail flicked back and forth. I felt safe enough to be vulnerable with him. "To be honest, I'm very stressed. I don't really know how to handle it. On the one paw, I want the crew to be happy. On the other, my daughter's life is on the line. I'm also not even sure if those concerns Walter mentioned are legitimate."

"Well," he said. "Those concerns could be legitimate, so it's something to take seriously and look into. However, I've seen this sort of thing before. Typically, but not always, one critter will take on the role of a so-called elected spokescritter of the crew. They bring up plenty of concerns to the captain. Sometimes they're legitimate, but often, they are just presenting their own thoughts as those of the team. Sometimes they do this to get promoted into a leadership position. Other times, they do it to be a hero for the rest of the team. I'm not saying that's the case currently. I'm just sharing a couple perspectives."

"So how do we determine which perspective is correct?"

"To be honest," Leo said. "Critter management is not my specialty. I know plenty about sailing and how to organize a crew, but that's where my expertise stops."

I sighed, glancing down at the blank parchment on the desk. This conversation wasn't going to be as fruitful as I'd hoped.

"However," Leo said, causing me to look back up. "Seafarers who travel these passages almost always seek wisdom during their journey. As a result, a sage operates in each of the ports we are visiting. Some sages are better than others, but these are some of the smartest raccoons I've met, especially as we travel further north. When we reach Dormeadow, I suggest you seek out the local sage and explain the situation. You'll get some direction."

I had heard of sages before. Growing up, I even saw a few wandering sages come through my hometown. These raccoons were supposedly the smartest ones out there, sharing deep wisdom with other critters. For a price, of course. Throughout my life, I never really believed it, attributing their good advice to luck more than anything. But with a critter as wise as Leo recommending it so confidently, it was worth a shot.

"Okay, thank you, I'll be sure to do that."

"Good."

Pause.

"Leo?"

"Yeah?"

"Is our work schedule too strict? Should we be giving them more rest time?"

Leo ran his fingers through his whiskers as he considered the question. "We can see how far we travel over the next few days. When I made the schedule, I made it so we would arrive in Enya in five weeks per your request. If everyone worked like Max and Oscar and Kia, we could absolutely increase the rest periods. But as I'm sure you've seen, many critters aren't trying as hard.

"Not that we should expect critters to work at full capacity every minute of the day, but some clearly are trying whereas others are not. If you can figure out how to make the team more productive, we can have a more relaxed and enjoyable schedule. But if not, I believe we'll need to keep to the current schedule if we want to make it to Enya in time."

"Okay, that's what I figured. I at least wanted to ask."

"Of course," Leo said. "Anything else?"

"No," I said. I was about to wish Leo a goodnight, but he opened his mouth to speak first.

"Okay. Are you up for a game of cards? I like to unwind after a busy day at sea." Before giving me a chance to respond, he took out a pouch strapped to his waist and dumped its contents on the desk. There was a stack of unique cards and some tiny wooden squares with numbers painted on them. "It's one of my favorite games. It's called The Eagle in the Mountains. Want to play?"

Why not? It would do me good to unwind a bit before bed.

"Sure," I said, moving the parchment and quill off the desk.

We played for several hours. Time flew by. That was the first time my mind stopped spinning since hearing my daughter's diagnosis.

# 6

Dormeadow was my kind of town. Calming, relaxing, the smell of fresh flora in the air—I loved it. Arrowhead, cricket ivy, and shoots of yellowed bamboo popped out of the water near the shore, waving under the gentle breeze to welcome the town's visitors. Lily pads lazily floated in the water between the rest of the greenery, though thankfully, I didn't see or hear any frogs. Although in such a serene environment, perhaps even frogs would be kind.

Rocks and pebbles rather than sand connected the sea to land. In Cherrystone, all the streets and shelters were placed with engineered precision, creating neat, orderly blocks. Here, the shelters appeared more like nature's decorative afterthought, with homes scattered haphazardly between all the various ponds, streams, hills, and plants.

I exited the gangway and walked down the short dock. The sun still slept beneath the horizon, yet only a couple vacant spots on the pier remained. Most ships would have to anchor at bay. Another shout-out to Leo for encouraging us to arrive early.

"Catch ya later!" Alyssa said as she darted off ahead, rushing to meet up with her sister for a breakfast forage.

The rest of the crew scattered about, each with their own agenda.

My one and only objective was speaking with the sage. Leo assured me he would handle getting supplies for the next leg of our voyage so I could focus on learning how to better lead the crew.

I continued walking down the smooth-pebbled path that weaved through the numerous ponds. Bridges conveniently stretched over smaller puddles, forming tiny archways for critters to cross. After crossing a couple of these bridges, I came to the first shop: Peeper Popper's Pretty Popular Popcorn. I was loving this village more and more.

I entered Peeper Popper's, and the salty, buttery aroma of freshly popped popcorn flooded my nose and seduced my tastebuds.

Passing by the buckets of flavored popcorn along the sides of the shop, I approached the friendly-looking mole at the counter. He looked at me with a larger-than-life smile.

"Goooooood morning, friend!"

"Hello!" I said. "This is the best popcorn I've ever smelled."

"It'll also be the best popcorn you've ever tasted! All popped fresh this and every morning," he said.

"How much?" The smell had officially seeped into my brain and temporarily assumed command.

"One kernel for two copper or two for three."

"I'll take the one."

"Which flavor?"

At least two dozen flavors flaunted themselves in the tiny shop, each trying to win my favor. Too many choices, so I resorted to my leave-it-to-fate technique for avoiding decision fatigue. "Surprise me."

The cheerful mole suddenly vanished down under the counter as if dodging a mosquito. I heard him shuffling through some cabinets, and then he popped back up with a huge kernel of popcorn.

"White popcorn misted with olive oil, sprinkled with flaky sea salt, and seasoned with fresh truffle!"

I grabbed the huge kernel with both paws and took a bite. As my teeth sunk into the tender kernel, my entire body tingled with happiness. Delicious.

With my hunger satiated, I refocused. "I'm looking for the local sage. Can you point me in the right direction?"

"Oh, you're looking for Raccoon Rita? Of course, it's simple. She's just around the pond. Exit the shop, cross the bridge, make a left, go straight, take the fourth bridge on the right, go straight, take the second left, climb the wooden ladder to the plateau, continue straight, go through the tunnel on the right, then you'll pop back out into the meadows. Look ahead, and you'll see her purple hut atop the knoll on the right. Easy peasy."

Moles talk fast, but this little critter talked even faster. After having him repeat those "simple" instructions a few times, I left his shop and did my best to follow them. After only a handful of wrong turns and asking other Dormeadow dwellers for directions, I arrived at Raccoon Rita's circular purple hut. Giant green leaves rested on the pointy roof, shielding the inside from the elements.

Standing atop the small knoll, I looked out over the meadow as the sun finally made its appearance, casting an orange glow over the wildlife and shelters of the seaside town.

"Come in," I heard a voice calling from inside the hut.

I pushed the green silk curtain that hung over the entrance aside and walked in.

The raccoon was sitting on the floor with a small round table in front of her. She beckoned for me to sit on the small square cushion in front of it, which I did. She then went to the side of the hut where she had a kettle resting over a small flame, poured some liquid into a thimble, and returned to the table. She set the thimble of hot liquid in front of me.

"Drink," she said.

I was rather thirsty from the popcorn, but my skepticism of sages held me back from accepting her offer. "No, thank you."

"Drink or leave," she said matter-of-factly.

"What is it?"

"Elderberry tea."

Her tone clearly indicated this conversation would end if I didn't drink, so I lifted the small round thimble with my paws and took a sip. It was surprisingly tasty. "It's very good, thank you."

"What can I help you with?" she asked.

I went to set the thimble of tea down, but she stopped me.

"Keep the tea in your paws until you finish it. It's a crisp morning. The warmth will help you relax and be more open with me."

"Okay," I said. After taking another sip, I explained my situation to her. I told her about the enchanted monocle, Walter's concerns, my personal apprehensions with some of the crew (like Collin), my anxiety about keeping others happy (like Artemis), and so on. The warm tea really did get me to open up quicker than I expected. Or maybe my desperation for answers was the culprit. Either way, getting everything out in the open felt good.

Rita didn't say a word the entire time I spoke. After I finished, I took the last sip of tea and hesitantly set the empty thimble on the table, eyeing her carefully to make sure she didn't object to my doing so.

"Where did you get the enchanted monocle?" she asked.

"A wandering vendor shrew named Rico," I responded.

"Keep him close. He is wiser than he lets on." She got up, grabbed my empty thimble of tea, filled it as well as a small cup for herself, and returned to the table. After handing my tea to me and taking a sip of her own, she began.

"The monocle will help you greatly on your voyage," she said. "Broadly speaking, there are three types of team members. For seafolk like yourself, I like to call them rowers, watchers, and sinkers.

"Rowers are the hard-working, passionate fellas who are actively moving the team and ship forward. Watchers are those critters who fit into the background. They help the team, but they don't go out of their way to go above and beyond. And then…there are the sinkers."

Rita's eyes narrowed, her head lowered, and her voice deepened.

"The sinkers are the ones who, if you don't intervene, will actively work to sink the ship. They're toxic to the team, and if you don't stop them, they will run your team and ship aground."

Rowers, watchers, sinkers. I repeated the words a few times in my head to commit them to memory.

"The rowers," she continued, "are great. You can leave them be, they don't need any motivation from you. But for the watchers and especially the sinkers, you need to stay on them to make sure they're pulling their weight. If you leave them be, others will get discouraged, and your team will crumble. If you're a good leader, you can motivate many of the watchers to become rowers and the sinkers to become watchers or even rowers. Your goal should be to have a team full of rowers."

"How can I do that?" I asked. "How can I turn sinkers into rowers?"

"Spend more time with them," she said. "You don't need to spend time with the rowers, so all your time should be focused on the watchers and sinkers. If you don't have time to focus on both, pick the sinkers. They're the ones who need your time the most so they don't bring down the ship."

Something inside me didn't like what she was saying. I enjoyed my conversations with Leo, Alyssa, Kia, and Max. Talking to Walter, Collin, Lilly, and the other watchers and sinkers drained my energy. The thought of spending less time with the rowers and more time with the sinkers didn't sound particularly enjoyable.

But Raccoon Rita was a sage, someone Leo trusted. I was just a weaver thrown into the suit of a captain. What did I know?

"Okay," I said. "So when I'm talking to watchers and sinkers, what should I say to motivate them to do better?"

For the next hour or so, Rita went over various techniques for motivating my crew. Hearing actionable advice like that helped make me feel better, though the thought of spending less time with rowers and more with sinkers still didn't sit well with me. But I was determined to try it. Maybe I would be pleasantly surprised.

After we finished, I paid the raccoon a silver for her time and stepped outside into the warming morning sun. As I began walking back to the ship, my mind replayed our conversation several times, thinking how I would incorporate all her advice.

I would get to work immediately. As soon as we set sail that afternoon, I was determined to talk to all the sinkers and come up with a plan to get them more motivated and working harder. Walter would be a tough one. He probably wanted recognition for getting the crew more breaks, so essentially telling him to work harder and stop complaining probably wouldn't make him super thrilled.

While walking, I noticed a little shop called Ponds n' Puddles with a mug of cordial painted on its sign. I really liked this little village. This could be a good place to raise Ella after she healed. I stepped into the shop for a drink and some breakfast. Afterwards, I explored the village a bit more, mingling with some of my crew as I bumped into them, and then made my way back to the ship. Shortly after the sun slipped into its noon position, we set back out into the sea.

# 7

Collin sat across from me in my quarters, his unkempt beige fur jutting out in every direction. This served as my first conversation with a sinker since speaking with Rita.

I hated conflict, though I didn't quite realize just how much until this moment.

"How's it going?" I asked, mostly to say something pleasant and delay the hard stuff a few more seconds.

"Fine," he said, unimpressed.

"We seem to be making good time overall?" I said/asked.

"Yeah, I guess."

Sigh. No more small talk.

"So…" I said, mentally flipping through the rolodex of pointers Rita had given me, trying to find the right words. "I wanted to talk to you about something."

"Yeah, I kind of got the hint when you told me you wanted to talk to me."

Fair enough. I coughed, clearing my throat, trying my best not to come across as weak.

"How do you feel the effort you put into the voyage compares to the others?" I asked.

"What do you mean?"

I looked at him for a moment. How else could I word that? "I mean, do you feel you put in the same effort as everyone else? More? Less?"

"About the same."

"Really?"

"Yes. Why? Do you feel differently?"

I took a breath, trying to choose my words carefully. "I feel like you could be doing more."

"What makes you say that?"

"Well, how fast do you feel you row compared to the others?"

"It sounds like you have an opinion already. Why don't you cut to the chase and say what you want to say."

This was not going well.

"It seems like you may not be as productive. When rowing, you don't move as fast as the others, and even more, you just don't seem to be trying as hard either. Same with fishing, cooking, and cleaning."

"That's because the schedule is too tight. We don't get enough rest time."

"I did speak with Leo about this, and he indicated that this schedule is very typical for seafarers. In fact, he erred on the side of giving more rest periods than most crews because we value the team and want to make sure we take care of everyone. With the speed everyone is moving, we must keep the rest time limited so we can reach Enya in time. However, if we can pick up the pace, we could take more time for rest."

Collin's nose twitched; he quickly licked his paw and then ran it over his nose a couple times.

"Once you give us more rest time," he said, "I'll work harder."

"I can't do that because if I give you more rest time and you *don't* work harder, we won't reach Enya in time."

"So we'll get there a few days later, big deal."

"I need to make it there within five weeks. That's the entire purpose of his voyage."

"That's *your* purpose," Collin said. "I was hired to get this ship to Enya and back in one piece, which is no easy feat, and for rather meager pay. You're lucky I joined this crew in the first place. I refuse to work harder unless you give us more rest time. Or more copper."

Collin stood up, indicating he was ready for this conversation to end.

I stood up as well. "Even though you are getting more breaks now than you would on most voyages?"

"Most voyages aren't going to Enya," he said, walking towards the door.

My mind raced, again flipping through my mental files of things to say, but by the time I gathered my thoughts, he had left. I plopped back down into my chair and sighed heavily. There were six more sinkers and seven watchers with whom I needed to talk. This was not fun. I would much rather have been spending my time talking with Kia, Alyssa, and the other rowers. I walked away from those conversations happier, typically with new knowledge or insights. Now, after talking with just one sinker, my head hurt.

Maybe I just got unlucky with my first conversation. Perhaps the next would go better.

I needed to get up and move to restore some energy, so I stood up, stretched my thin arms up towards the ceiling and then over to the sides. My back gave two satisfying cracks, already providing some relief.

After walking out of my quarters, I made my way down the hall and then up the stairs to the deck. Oscar bumped into me at the top of the stairs.

"Hello, captain!" he said eagerly. The excitement in his voice refreshed me like iced coconut water on a hot sunny day. Oscar was a rower and one of the hardest-working critters aboard.

"Hey, Oscar!"

"Do you have a sec? I have an idea for how we can catch more fish."

He was a gerbil's breath away from jumping into the details before I held up my paw to stop him.

"Oscar, I'd love to hear it, I truly would. But I have several other crewmates I need to talk to first."

"But I think this could really help us get more fish," he continued. "The more fish the crew eats instead of just nuts and grains, the more energized they'll be. I think it could help increase crew morale."

"I'd love to hear it," I said. "I just need to have these other conversations first. Is that okay?"

He sighed, clearly disappointed.

"Hey," I said with a smile. "I'll meet up with you by the end of the day, I promise."

A smile returned to his face. "Okay, Captain. You know where to find me!"

He scurried off to his next posting. I stayed there a minute, thinking how enjoyable it would be to speak with Oscar instead of the other sinkers. This was only temporary, just until everyone worked with the same, or at least similar, effort. Although I certainly had my doubts Collin would ever turn into an Oscar.

Augusto started walking past me, fishing rod in hand, ready for his fishing shift. He was the next sinker on my list.

"Hey, Augusto," I said.

He turned to face me, his long brown fur blowing nearly horizontally under the wind. He had the longest fur of any of the crew, a veritable mane compared to my own.

"Can I talk to you for a sec?" I asked.

"Sure," he said, and followed me to my cabin.

My conversation with Augusto went a little better than that with Collin. Augusto seemed like he *wanted* to do better but was paranoid everyone else was out to get him. We talked in circles for a while, but he eventually agreed to not assume the worst in others. Hopefully, if he felt more respected by his crewmates, he would be motivated to put in more effort.

After Augusto, I managed to get through chatting with all the sinkers except for Walter. I needed to save him for the next day when I had more energy. Most of the conversations went pretty well, with each critter thanking me for chatting with them and promising to improve.

After my last meeting, I decided to head out and find Oscar. I wanted to end the day on a positive note talking about fishing.

When I opened my cabin door, Leo and Artemis stood waiting for me.

"Captain," Leo said in a soft voice lacking its usual warmth.

"We need to talk," Artemis said, and then pushed her way into my cabin.

I looked at Leo, who glanced back at me, a defeated expression on his face. I stepped aside, let Leo walk past, and then closed the door.

Artemis paced back and forth in front of the desk while Leo took a seat. She didn't even wait for me to reach my chair before she started.

"Something needs to change," she said, giving me a menacing look.

"What happened?" I asked, sitting down.

"Half this crew doesn't want to be here," she said. "They are one of the laziest bunches of mice I've ever seen. Not only that, but when I try to teach them how to work more effectively, they talk back to me, claiming I have no authority to boss them around. I've been on dozens of voyages, and I've never seen such a disrespectful group of critters."

She paused, waiting for me to say something. Her ferocity froze me in place, rendering me unable to find words.

"And you," she said, pointing directly at me, sending a chill through my veins. "You're enabling this. When these critters talk back to me and the captain does nothing, they take that as a signal to continue. Not only continue, but advance. They keep pushing and pushing, seeing how much they can get away with, and when you do nothing, it only encourages the behavior."

"I spoke with several of them today specifically about their work ethic," I defended, although it sounded more like a plea for her to calm down.

"Did you discipline them?"

"Well, no, but—"

"Did you threaten to kick them off the crew?"

"No, but don't you—"

"Then all you did was waste time," she said, slamming her white paw on the desk. "You need to *act*, not just talk to critters like these. The strictest captains have the most able and happy crews. Everyone pulls their weight, everyone motivates each other, and the voyages are successful. When captains try to please everyone, tiptoe around discipline, and allow the slackers to do as they please, everything falls apart. We'll never make it to Enya like this."

When she finished, the three of us remained silent for a few breaths. I glanced at Leo, hoping he would throw me a lifeline. He seemed to get my message, for he said, "While I think Artemis is being a little too intense given how early we are on the voyage, she does have a point. Kia and Alyssa have also both commented that they are getting frustrated with how hard they're working compared to the rest. I don't think we need to take it to Artemis's extreme and throw everyone who makes a mistake overboard, but if they don't start putting in more effort, something needs to happen. Something more than just conversations.

"That being said," his gaze turned towards Artemis, "it's only the third day, so I feel we owe it to the critters to give them a chance before passing judgment."

"Day three of a thirty-five-day journey is nearly ten percent complete," Artemis said quickly, though some of the venom had dissipated from her voice. Her tail swung back and forth with a quick flick.

"Well, I think the captain has received your message and understands the situation, am I right?" Leo asked, turning to me.

I nodded.

"Good," Leo said as he grabbed his walking stick off the desk. "Then I say we all get some rest. There's not much we're going to solve right now in this room."

Without waiting for any replies, Leo rose to his feet.

"Fine," Artemis said, then she looked directly into my eyes. "I won't tolerate this for too much longer, captain."

Artemis rushed past Leo and left the cabin. After she disappeared, Leo turned to me. "You alright?"

"I'll be fine," I said. "I agree with her that something needs to happen. It's just… a lot."

"Would you like me to stay and talk? Or maybe we could play a game of The Eagle in the Mountains to give your mind a rest?"

"No… I would prefer some alone time tonight. I've had a long day."

Leo smiled. "Tomorrow, then. Have a good night."

"Goodnight, Leo."

Leo left, and I immediately dragged myself to my bed and collapsed. Today was rough. Tomorrow would hopefully be better.

# 8

"What were you thinking?!" Kia screamed at Walter as the morning sun broke the horizon.

"It's not that big a deal," Walter said defensively. "We got a little off track—"

"A *little?* This sets us back at least eight hours, if not more."

"We'll be fine. We were just having some fun."

"Well, I'm sure no one will be thanking you when we have to pull extra shifts to make up for it."

This officially shattered my hope of a better day. Walter thought it a good idea to let the night crews only work half their shifts. As a result, the current had pulled the ship off course. Leo and Alyssa were still trying to get our bearings to see exactly how much, but Walter's decision clearly put us behind schedule.

"Walter," I said during the next opening I found in their conversation. "Come below deck with me so we can talk, please."

They swapped a few more verbal jabs at one another before Walter reluctantly followed me to my cabin. On the way down, we bumped into Oscar, who had just woken and was heading to the kitchen to make breakfast for the crew.

"Hey, captain!" he said enthusiastically. "Is now a good time to chat about my fishing ideas?"

Ugh. I had completely forgotten to talk to him last night. The meeting with Leo and Artemis had clouded my mind, making me forget my commitment to Oscar.

"I'm sorry," I said. "I need to talk with Walter. I'm sorry I didn't come find you last night. We'll talk tonight, okay?"

He sighed, clearly disappointed. When he saw Walter behind me, he decided not to push it.

"Okay," he said, sounding hopeful. "I'll see you tonight."

A pain bloomed inside my chest for letting him down. If only he knew how much I'd rather be talking to him about fishing than talking to Walter about…whatever we were about to talk about.

Walter and I entered my cabin and sat at opposite sides of the desk. Although the cabin was nice, I grew tired of spending so much time there rather than outside on deck.

"Did you hear how she spoke to me?" Walter asked, his tail flicking back and forth. "She humiliated me in front of the entire crew. You better be talking to her afterwards. This is unacceptable."

"I agree she could've handled it better, and I will address that with her. But she's not wrong. What you did really set us back."

"I tried telling you before that the crew needs more time to rest. You weren't doing anything, so I had to."

"What exactly did you do?"

"Well, I could tell everyone was pretty exhausted, so I suggested we all take a break, have a snack, and play a few harmless games."

"Did anyone tell you they were exhausted, or did you just assume?"

"I mean no one explicitly said that because no one wants to be viewed as lazy. But it's a leader's job to notice when their team's overworked."

I brought my paws to the side of my face and rubbed my temples. So many critters and perspectives involved. Trying to accommodate one set of needs always created others, like cutting the head off a hydra.

"You need to run things like this past me and Leo first," I said. "I spent all day yesterday talking to the crew, motivating and encouraging them to work a little harder so we can switch up the schedule to allow for more rest. And then this happens, which not only set us back but also results in us needing to make the schedule even stricter to catch up."

"Hey," he said, continuing his defensive tone. "I'm just doing what's necessary to prevent a mutiny."

"From now on," I said, returning my paws to my desk. "Run any changes in the schedule past me or Leo first, alright? At a bare minimum, we need to be kept in the loop and on the same page."

"I'll try," he said. "But I'm putting the needs of the crew above your or even my personal desires."

"Look," I said. "It's my number-one priority to make sure the crew is happy and motivated. I'll be spending all day today again having one-on-ones with everyone to figure out a work schedule that's agreeable. I'll do everything I can to give critters as many breaks as possible, but I need you working with me, not against me."

"As long as the crew is happy, so am I," he said, not really committing to anything.

"Okay," I said. I had little confidence we understood each other, but I didn't really know what else to say.

Before he left, Walter had several issues to bring up, most of which were supposedly issues the crew brought to his attention, since he was their spokesmouse. We went through all the issues, and I promised to investigate everything. That's all I did, investigate things. They should have referred to me as *investigator* rather than *captain*.

Walter left, and I spent the rest of the day talking to all the watchers, and even a couple of the sinkers a second time. Every meeting went over its allotted time, causing me to miss lunch and be late to nearly every meeting. Problems sprouted up everywhere. I didn't even know where to start. Even if I did, I didn't have time to actually do anything because meetings consumed my entire day.

Fortunately, the day came and went without another visit from Artemis. I couldn't imagine her fury with Walter's actions. She probably wanted me to fire him. Part of *me* wanted to fire him. But if the crew viewed him as a resource to relay their grievances to me and I fired him, what kind of message would that send? Who else would quit as a result? It wasn't fun dealing with an unhappy crew, but it was better than being stuck at port without any crew at all.

When night shift arrived, I again ran into Oscar, who seemed just as eager to share his fishing ideas. I still had one more meeting and hadn't eaten all day save for a little toast and jam in the morning, so I told him we'd have to find another time. I felt horrible, but I just didn't have the time or the energy.

It was easy to listen to Rita's various tips and tricks, but nothing compared to experiencing it.

# 9

On the fifth day, we arrived in Nibbletown in the late afternoon, about ten hours behind schedule. Between Walter's episode at night and the overall drop in productivity due to weakening morale, the voyage's outlook—meaning Ella's outlook—darkened.

After we docked, I was about to head down the gangway when Rico popped up from the side. "Imagine walking around with *thiiis*." He held up two cloth slippers with protective leather soles on the bottom.

"No, thank you," I said. I wasn't in the mood.

"Nibbletown is known for jagged and pointy rocks," the shrew warned as I began walking down the gangway.

"I'm fine," I insisted. I was too busy to deal with him right now. We were late. I needed to talk to the sage before they closed. Plus, we needed supplies, food, and then we had to leave port quickly to stay on schedule.

As I left the gangway, I remembered Rico was leaving us at Nibbletown. Part of me wanted to go back to say farewell and thank the shrew for his help, but I didn't have time.

Wait. Stop. I did have time. I would make time. This was important.

I turned around and started walking back up when Artemis appeared at the top of the gangway and stormed towards me.

"I quit," she said.

"You quit?" I asked.

She stopped a few whiskers' length in front of me.

"Yes, I quit, and Alyssa is coming with me as well. This crew is too toxic. You clearly don't have what it takes to lead a crew of this size, let alone lead us to Enya. You seem nice enough, and maybe you'll eventually learn, but I'm done."

Without waiting for a response, she walked off the gangway and headed into town.

Everything in my peripheral vision darkened. I could only see a narrow spot in front of me. What was I going to do now? What if some of the crew heard her? What if they quit too? It wouldn't be the sinkers who would quit; it would be critters like Kia, Max, maybe even... Leo?

I should've listened to Artemis more. I should've just started firing all the lazy mice. But maybe they weren't lazy at all. Maybe they just needed good leadership. Maybe I was the problem.

Anger built up inside me as I clenched my fists. Although Artemis wasn't the nicest mouse aboard, she was a rower, one of the hardest-working crewmates. Losing her stung.

The thud of Leo's peg leg on the gangway yanked me back from my spiraling thoughts and returned me to the present. As my vision cleared, I saw him approaching and said immediately, "Artemis and Alyssa quit."

"Yes, lad," he said, "they told me just before telling you. How are you doing?"

"Not good," I said. "What if more follow?"

"I don't think anyone else will quit right now."

"What do you mean *right now?*"

"Well," he said, stepping off the gangway and onto the wooden pier, "Crew morale is slipping. If we don't address it soon, I suspect more will leave."

My legs started quivering. I wanted to disappear and go back to weaving. This sucked.

"Cheer up," Leo said, though his enthusiasm sounded forced. "Things like this happen all the time during voyages. Each port we visit has a Guild Hall where critters looking for seafaring jobs congregate when ships come in. It's getting late, so why don't you go visit the sage now and then meet me back at the Guild Hall so we can find some new crew members. Savvy?"

If Leo quit, I didn't know what I'd do. Hopefully, I'd never have to find out.

"Alright," I said. "Thank you, Leo. Really, I mean it."

Leo smiled his typical warm smile. "Of course. We're in this to-gether."

He patted me on the back so hard it took the wind out of me, and then he ventured off into the village.

After asking a nearby dockhand for directions to the sage (down the main street and take the fifth street on the right, much simpler than Dormeadow), I left the dock and entered the streets of Nibbletown.

Nibbletown was known for, well, nibbles. Located perfectly at the intersection of several rivers and streams, ships frequently stopped at this port, bringing exotic foods, herbs, and spices from distant lands. With so much culinary diversity, critters adept at cooking frequently stayed here for many seasons to hone their craft and occasionally even open their own grub spot.

An unfortunate side effect of all the tourism, sharp objects, from broken bottles to shattered clay cups and plates, polluted the ground. Every other step sent a jolt of pain through my paws as I stepped on the jagged edge of some material or another. Rico wasn't wrong when he suggested some paw protection here. Too late now.

"Hey, Martin!" Alex called. I looked over and saw the little mouse about to enter a shop.

"Hey, Alex!" I said. Seeing another hard-working crewmate happy and upbeat calmed my mind for a moment. "What are you up to?"

"Checking out this spice shop. Want to join me?"

"I'd love to," I said, "but I need to see the sage and then I'm meeting up with Leo."

"No worries! I'm super excited to see what kind of spices they have. I'm on cooking duty tonight, so prepare the crew for some yummy grub!"

"With your passion for cooking, I'm surprised you don't live here."

"I'd love to, but it's so darn expensive. I'm going to use the copper I get from this voyage to enter a culinary contest in my hometown. The winning prize is an apprenticeship here in Nibbletown. So if you ever need someone to pull extra hours in the galley, I'm your mouse. I could use all the practice I can get."

"I'll keep that in mind," I said.

"Okay, well, I won't hold you up. Catch ya later, Cap'n!"

This was what I needed. More conversations like this. Even without the monocle, I could tell Alex was a rower. We needed more Alexes on board.

After following the simple directions, I arrived at the sage's hut, which was the exact same shape and size as the one in Dormeadow, only painted yellow. No one was waiting, although I could hear the sage speaking with a critter inside. I waited a few moments for them to wrap up, and then I entered the hut and sat at the table in front of the raccoon.

This raccoon was bigger than Rita. He sat with his large, poofy black and grey-colored tail curled around his waist and nestled in his lap. As in Dormeadow, a table to the side housed a tea kettle and cups, but this sage seemed rather uninterested in them.

"How may I help you?" he asked.

As before, I poured everything out. I confessed how much I hated talking to sinkers, how sad and worried I was that Alyssa and Artemis quit, how little time I was spending talking to the rowers, and how crew morale overall was slipping. I also shared about Walter, and how it seemed he was actively working against me, creating a rift between me and the rest of the crew.

The raccoon watched me as I talked, slowly and methodically running his claws through his fluffy tail. No matter how fast I talked or how intense my anger grew, his rhythm of petting his tail never changed. To me, the world was ending, but to him, this was just another day. Nothing I said seemed to rattle him. Perhaps my problems weren't as bad as I thought. Though maybe he'd react differently if his daughter's life was on the line.

After a moment of silence, he spoke.

"You seem quick to judge critters as rowers, watchers, and sinkers."

"Well, like I said, I have a monocle that—"

"You seem quick to judge critters as rowers, watchers, and sinkers."

I wasn't quite sure what to say, other than trying to repeat myself in a different way. "Yes, but it's only because of—"

"Don't justify," he said. "We aren't judging anyone or anything right now. We are just exploring reality. What is, is. What is not, is not. The reasoning does not matter, for now. Can we agree that you are quick to judge critters as rowers, watchers, and sinkers, regardless of why?"

I understood his point. "Yes."

"Good. Now, when you classify someone as a 'sinker,' what does that mean to you?"

"Well, Raccoon Rita said—"

"I didn't ask what Raccoon Rita said. I asked what it means to you."

"Ah, okay. Umm…a sinker is a critter who isn't working hard."

"Why would a critter not work hard?"

"Because they don't want to."

"Why would they not want to?"

"Because they're lazy." I felt rather immature for using the word *lazy*, but it was the best word I could think of at the time.

"That could be one reason," he allowed. "Let's explore a different possibility. Let's imagine a sinker is not lazy. Let's imagine this sinker wants to work hard, but isn't. What could explain that scenario?"

I thought about it for a second before responding. "Well, maybe they don't understand the job's expectations or how to complete certain tasks properly. Or perhaps they don't feel they're treated fairly, so they don't try as hard as they could."

The raccoon smiled, which caught me by surprise.

"Yes, young captain. Those are certainly valid possibilities. It's possible that a critter might appear to be a sinker but could, deep down, be a rower. When you are speaking with these critters, are you exploring those other possibilities, or are you simply delivering the message: 'work harder'?"

His words clicked with me: he made a fair point. I didn't need to verbally respond for him to continue.

"A critter could be a sinker on one crew but one of the finest rowers in another. Whether some critter is a sinker or rower is not a personality trait; it's more of a reflection of how that critter is operating in the specific environment. In fact, I don't think any critters are inherently sinkers: some just thrive in certain environments more than others. When you identify a sinker, it's usually not an issue with that critter—it's an issue with the environment.

"My advice to you is this: whenever a critter is not meeting your expectations, before you attribute blame to the critter, try attributing blame to yourself. You are guilty until proven innocent in this regard. Have you told them clearly what's expected? Have you ensured they understand your expectations?

"Have you ensured they've been properly trained? Do they have all the tools needed to complete the job? Is there anything you or anyone else is doing or not doing that's holding them back?

"You must look inwards towards yourself and exhaust all practical avenues for helping them do better before simply writing them off as sinkers."

Everything the sage said made sense, and I would incorporate his suggestions into my discussions with the crew. Part of me still felt unsettled. These bits of advice might make the conversations go a little smoother, but I still would be spending most of my time with critters who lacked motivation. Perhaps they lacked motivation because they didn't understand the job, but if they lacked motivation, would understanding make any impact? Even if I could somehow motivate them through a pep talk, how long would that motivation last? Would I need to keep talking with them over and over every time their motivation dipped, or would it permanently stay lifted?

"Something on your mind?" the sage asked.

He had given me a lot to think about and try out. It was very possible, potentially even probable, that my issues would go away by following his advice. My time with the sage was ending, and I didn't want to overstay my welcome.

"No, just taking in everything you said. This has been very helpful, thank you."

We shared a few parting words, I paid him, and then I left the tent and headed for the Guild Hall to meet up with Leo. On the way, I stopped at a grub stand to pick up a quick snack of roasted apples with some crumbled toasted walnuts and a drizzle of rosemary-infused honey. It tasted amazing for such a simple dish. I walked and ate, trying to leave as much time as needed for recruiting. Between the warm sweetness from each bite of the apples and the stinging pain from every sharp edge I stepped on, my mind had no chance to worry about anything.

When I reached the Guild Hall, I tossed away the thin cardboard basket, licked my paws clean, and went inside.

The hall resembled a spacious pub without the bar. Small barrels and circular tables scattered about the open room. Flaming lanterns dangled from the horizontal support beams, casting a warm glow throughout the massive area despite the sun nearly setting outside.

Probably three dozen critters chattered throughout the hall. All sorts of critters: mice, shrews, moles, rabbits, even a couple squirrels. Squirrels—some of the hardest working mammals around—were also the most expensive. If only I had more copper to pay the crew, I would hire a bunch of squirrels, let them do their thing, and then just focus on staying out of their way rather than spending all my time motivating everyone.

Next time, perhaps.

"Captain!" Leo called out, sitting on one of the barrels to the side. I approached him, and he immediately asked how it went with the sage. I explained everything we discussed, and he nodded at several points I made.

"That all makes sense," he said when I finished. "So are you feeling better?"

"A little, but we still need to get two crew members."

"Then let's take care of that," he said.

Reaching into my breast pocket, I pulled out my monocle, slipped it over my eye, and scanned the room. There were a variety of rowers, watchers, and sinkers everywhere. Each species contained critters of all three colors, except for the squirrels, of course: they were all tinted green.

I noticed something curious. For those critters in groups, the members of the group all seemed to have the same color. Rowers gathered with rowers, watchers with watchers. There may have been a couple critters of different colors commingling, but for the most part, they were all in separate groups.

"Look at those two," Leo said, pointing to a tall, darker mouse and a mole leaning against one of the support beams. Both green. "The mouse is a navigator, one who's sailed these seas countless times and is skilled at identifying the fastest and safest passages. With all his experience, he helped mapmakers draw their charts of the sea.

"The mole is a bard. His exceptional strength would be good for rowing, and his music would help lift morale. There have been a lot of studies showing seafarers work better and enjoy their work more with good music. What do you think?"

"That sounds great," I said. "Any idea what their rate is?"

"No, but why don't you go check? I'm sure it's something we can make work. Their talents would be well worth it."

That seemed like something I could do. I made my way over to the pair of critters, and as soon as they saw me, I immediately wanted them on my crew. They seemed friendly, offered wide smiles, and emitted positive energy that flowed into me.

"G'morning!" the taller mouse said.

"Good morning," I said. "It's a pleasure to meet both of you."

"My name's Patrick," the mouse said, and then he motioned to his friend. "And this guy's Ralph."

"I'm Martin," I said. As soon as I said my name, they exchanged glances as if they recognized me, although this was the first time we'd met. "I'm captain of the *Skimmer*, and I'm looking for two more crew on our voyage to Enya. My first mate, Leo, mentioned you're an expert navigator and you're a talented bard. I'd love to offer you both a position if you're interested."

Patrick smiled as I complimented him and his friend. "Thanks for the kind words, Martin, I appreciate it. We also appreciate the offer, but I'm afraid we'll have to pass."

His sudden rejection surprised me. "No worries," I said quickly, trying to mask my surprise. "Are you not looking for crew positions?"

"We are," Patrick said. He then paused and looked down at Ralph. After a second, Ralph gave Patrick a subtle nod, as if giving him permission to say something. Patrick took a breath and then looked back at me. "Look, Martin, you seem very nice and kind, which is rather rare in captains these days. Artemis and Alyssa were just here. Artemis is a close friend of mine, so whenever we bump into each other, we always catch up.

"She told me she just left your crew. She didn't say anything bad about you as a captain, just that the overall work ethic and team morale was rather low. I was the captain of a voyage once, and I know how difficult it is to lead a team, especially when morale is shaky. So I empathize with you.

"That being said, at this point we're not really looking to join a crew where most of the team isn't in sync. I've been on voyages like that before, and it's just not any fun, especially for critters like Ralph and me who put our all into everything we do. I hope that makes sense."

I nodded. Despite my disappointment, their reasoning made sense. "I understand. Thank you for sharing that. It's hard to hear and is obviously not the answer I wanted, but I appreciate you being honest with me."

"Of course," Patrick said, sounding relieved I didn't take his critique too harshly. "You seem pretty smart. I'm sure you'll figure it out. Maybe I'll join you on the next voyage."

I forced a smile, we spoke for a few more minutes, and then I retreated to Leo, defeat plastered over my face. We spoke for a little and then began scouting for new crew members. We split up and approached several critters, explained our voyage, and tried to find replacements for Artemis and Alyssa.

Many of the other captains brought their crews into the Guild Hall so potential new recruits could get to know them and their culture. As I watched, I noticed that again, like-minded critters seemed to attract one another. The rowers typically joined crews consisting primarily of rowers, watchers attracted watchers, and sinkers attracted sinkers.

If I could somehow find a way to lift everyone's spirits, provide them the tools and training they needed, and keep them motivated enough to become rowers, I could then bring them with me to future Guild Halls to attract more high-quality crewmates. If not, it seemed like I would be attracting critters without any real passion or desire to work on a ship.

I needed to figure out how to manage a crew. Quickly.

We eventually hired two critters. According to the monocle, one was yellow and the other, red. I wasn't very thrilled, but at least we had a full crew.

When we left the Guild Hall, I noticed Rico peddling some merchandise to a passerby. Lifting one of my back paws to see the underside, I noticed small cuts and bruises all over. I probably should have bought his paw protectors before we left.

"I'll meet you back aboard," I told Leo, and waved goodbye to him and the two new shipmates. I approached Rico and waited until he successfully completed the transaction.

"'ello, Cap'n!" he said.

"Looks like you're making out nicely in Nibbletown," I said.

He responded by lifting a coin pouch and jiggling it a couple times, indicating its fullness.

I laughed. "Glad to hear. I decided to take you up on your offer for the paw protectors. I probably should've listened to you earlier. That is if they're still available?"

"Of course," he said. He stuffed his hand inside his massive, thick coat, fishing through his numerous pouches of knickknacks, and proudly displayed the slippers.

"How much?" I asked, pulling out my own coin pouch, significantly less bountiful than his.

"I have a proposal," he said. "I decided I want to travel all the way to Enya."

I looked at him surprised. "Really? Why?"

"Well, originally, I just wanted to see Nibbletown, but now I'm realizing the value of visiting the ports in the northern regions, especially Anchorville. Very few ships ever go that far, so I can only imagine the unique wares I'd find. The cost for me to visit those ports on my own wouldn't make economic sense, so if I can hitch a ride with you, the slippers are yers for free. Furthermore, I'll chip in on the supplies for the crew since I understand I'm another mouth to feed. Deal?"

Part of me felt relief Rico wanted to stay with us. Even though we didn't interact a lot, he felt like a friend. The only crew member aboard without pay, he clearly *wanted* to be there. Since he didn't technically work for me, I felt more at ease talking to him; I didn't need to watch my words too carefully. Plus, Racoon Rita advised me to keep him nearby.

"Deal," I said. He gave me the slippers, I put them on, and together, we returned to the *Skimmer*.

# 10

As soon as we left Nibbletown and sailed for the fishing village of Dingle, I sat by myself in my cabin and came up with a new plan. When we started the voyage, of the twenty-one crewmates (not counting Rico or myself), we had seven rowers, seven watchers, and seven sinkers. Now, with Artemis and Alyssa leaving, we were down to five rowers, eight watchers, and eight sinkers.

When I first spoke with the watchers and sinkers, I essentially told them to do better. This time, following the most recent sage's advice, I was going to focus on things that *I* was or was not doing that was holding them back. Before assigning blame to them, I needed to look inward at what I could be doing better. I needed to focus on the environment, for which I as the captain was responsible.

I made notes of everything I knew about each watcher and sinker: their goals, passions, anything I could remember. Over the next couple of days, I had lengthy conversations with all of them. These conversations went much smoother than the ones prior, though my time still wasn't being spent the way I'd wanted.

On the plus side, Augusto, the critter who felt the other crewmates were being critical of him, upgraded himself to a watcher. That was about the only positive change.

One thing that bothered me was Oscar. When walking the ship at one point, I noticed Oscar's color had changed to yellow, indicating he had switched from a rower to a watcher. This was rather disheartening. I knew the reason: he had been wanting to talk to me about fishing, and I kept putting him off. Now that he had become a watcher, a conversation with him became more urgent, but I wasn't proud that it took him slipping for me to prioritize him.

Nonetheless, I continued filling my days with talking to critters who weren't performing well. We'd have lengthy conversations, I'd feel good about them, things would improve for a little while, but then as time passed, they'd slip back to their old performance levels. I found myself starting to have the same conversations over and over with worsening results.

I started coming up with checklists and policies for the crew to follow while working at each station to make sure I was properly communicating expectations. Those took a lot of time to create—again, time I wish I could've been spending with the rowers—but I finally got them done and felt pretty good about them.

However, that led to a new slew of problems. Now that we had checklists and policies, all the critters knew what the expectations were, but what should happen if a critter didn't do something properly? Constant discipline risked creating a stressful work environment that put everyone on edge. But if I let things slide, that sent a message that the checklists and policies were optional. In the latter case, the critters who *did* complete the checklists and followed the policies would get angry that I wasn't enforcing them.

Countless problems like this with no right answer continuously pelted me throughout the days. I felt like I was standing outside in a hailstorm, day after day, unable to find relief.

My sole enjoyment of the voyage was playing The Eagle in the Mountains with Leo at night. No matter how rough my day was and no matter how much my head hurt, I always made time for a round or two with Leo.

When we eventually made it to Dingle, we had fallen behind schedule by two full days, primarily due to the lack of work ethic. Aside from Oscar slipping from a rower to a watcher, two watchers had become sinkers, and many of the rowers were getting upset with how hard they worked compared to everyone else. To make matters worse, as soon as we docked, Kia and Max, both rowers, quit.

If I wasn't doing this to save my daughter, *I* would have quit. No part of me wanted to continue, but I had to keep trying.

We went to the Guild Hall, and, as the captains did in Nibbletown, I invited my crew to tag along so potential recruits could get to know them. At this point, however, I only had two rowers left: Leo and Alex. As in Nibbletown, I noticed crews with primarily rowers attracted rowers and those with watchers attracted watchers. Unfortunately, with the largest group of my crew acting as sinkers, I was forced to hire two sinkers to replace Kia and Max.

My crew now consisted of two rowers, eight watchers, and eleven sinkers.

Leo advised me to seek counsel with the local sage. I was so disgusted with myself and my poor performance as a captain that I didn't have the spirit to receive any more advice. I had been doing a pretty great job at failing to use any of the previous advice properly, so I didn't see the point.

Instead of visiting the sage, while walking through the village, I noticed a weaver supply shop down the street. At last finding something that gave me comfort, I approached the shop and entered. The smell of fresh linen and silk filled the air and pulled me closer, inviting me to stay a while and browse.

My gaze casually drifted from the looms to the fabrics to the combs and needles and dowels. My paws enjoyed the various textures of the materials and tools—soft, hard, pointy, smooth, warm, cold, all the sensations felt great. This was where I wanted to be, to escape into a world with my tools and get lost in my craft. My work made all my customers happy, and I didn't have to rely on or manage anyone else.

My comfort quickly morphed into something more sinister as I blamed the crew for pulling me away from my weaving, preventing me from working on my craft. I had brought some of my weaving supplies aboard, but I spent all my time and energy trying to motivate them and keep the peace, which left me no time for relaxing or weaving. All I did was give, and all they did was take. Even Leo, as kind and generous as he was, never gave me any specific advice on what I should do. With all the voyages he'd been on, surely he must have known more than he was telling me.

Ugh. I put my paws over my eyes, blacking out my view. I pressed inward until it hurt. I hated the mouse I was becoming. I knew I wasn't being fair. I shouldn't be blaming the crew, especially Leo. But I couldn't control how I felt.

Maybe I just needed some sleep. Maybe some rest would do me good.

Not wanting to slip further into negativity, I left the weaver shop, got some grub, and boarded the *Skimmer*. A few hours later, we left for the next village. My confidence in successfully completing this voyage and saving my daughter had never been lower.

# 11

"We're running low on food," Melvin complained. Initially a watcher, now a sinker.

"Lilly was in charge of provisions," Alex said, fortunately still a rower, though barely hanging on.

"No one told me how much to get," Lilly said defensively, another watcher-turned-sinker.

"We went over it three times!" Alex said.

"It must've just been a miscommunication," Lilly defended.

"We say that every time a problem arises," Alex said. "Simply labeling a problem or a mistake as *miscommunication* isn't solving anything. That's just used to avoid anyone taking accountability."

"Well," Oscar said, sadly another rower-turned-sinker. "Had the captain actually taken the time to listen to my ideas about fishing, we'd have plenty of food right now."

Everyone turned quiet. No member of the crew had ever publicly ridiculed me like that. They all focused on me, waiting for my reaction.

At this point, I didn't care. It had been several days passed since we left Nibbletown, and every aspect of this voyage had deteriorated. Ubiquitous problems kept me up at night, robbing me of any rest. Sleep-deprived, hungry, and exhausted, my hope slipped away, replaced by a phantom of negative energy seeping into my brain. The darkness flowed freely through my mind, tainting every thought with toxicity. Whenever I tried to purge it, the foul presence sunk its claws into my brain, injecting me with a headache-inducing poison. After enduring so much pain, I stopped fighting and surrendered to it.

My crew's argument failed to penetrate my thoughts. I had just surfaced on deck to grab Walter, not to deal with their problems.

"Walter, please come with me," I said.

"Aren't you going to say something?" Lilly asked.

"Not now."

"Well, I'm not rowing anymore until you listen to us and resolve these issues. I'm tired of you constantly brushing our concerns aside."

"I'll talk with you after Walter," I said.

"Are you okay with some of the crew not working in the meantime?" Alex said. "It looks like a storm's coming."

I glanced in the direction of the darkened clouds. They seemed far enough away, not likely to reach us. They also could simply be rain clouds. Besides, we had sailed through storms before.

"Alex," I said, looking back at him, trying to control my temper. "I can only solve one problem at a time. I'm going to talk to Walter, and then I'll talk to Lilly, and then I'll talk to you. Unless you'd rather I try talking to all three at once?"

As soon as those words left my mouth, I regretted it. Alex and Leo were the only two rowers left, the only crewmates who cared. My sarcasm certainly didn't help. In response, he just scoffed and walked up to the quarterdeck where Leo manned the helm.

Walter and I went below deck to my cabin. As soon as we walked in, he started talking: "You are losing control of—"

"I can clearly see that," I interrupted, not in the mood for lectures. We stood on opposite sides of my desk. "Look, Walter, I don't know what else to do with you. Every time I bring you to my cabin, you express all these concerns without ever giving me any specific details. Then I touch base with everyone so I can address them, and they all deny having those concerns in the first place."

"That's because they don't feel comfortable being honest with you."

"Then what am I supposed to do?! If no one is honest with me, how can I help them?"

"Why don't you trust me?"

"Because none of what you tell me is verifiable. You're the only mouse aboard this ship who hears these things and claims no one feels comfortable being honest with me. Why haven't they told Leo? Why not Alyssa when she was still with us?"

"Are you calling me a liar?"

I slammed my fist on the desk, anger bubbling over my skin. "I don't know. I don't know what to believe anymore. There are so many rumors and secrets. All I do is listen to complaint after complaint after complaint. No one offers solutions. No one seems to want things to get better. Everyone just wants to complain."

Walter looked at me with surprise. He had never seen me lose it like this. *I* had never seen myself lose it like this. Frustration had completely overthrown any sense of calmness or self-control, which made me say all the wrong things. But the heck with it. When I said all the right things, no good came from it. Nothing I said or did made any positive changes, so I stopped trying. Or caring.

We kept going back and forth for at least an hour, probably more, and then Alex barged into my cabin without knocking.

"Captain! We have a problem!"

# 12

Walter and I rushed to the upper deck in Alex's wake.

The storm had caught up with us. Up above, an imposing wall of dark clouds pushed through the sky. Flashes of lightning washed through the darkness, each flash accompanied by an eruption of thunder that reverberated through my bones. Angry waves charged towards us, an army of whitecaps that held no mercy for any sailor nor ship.

Alex had been right to warn me of the storm. How could I be so careless? All the issues and problems had distracted me. Had Patrick, the navigator from Nibbletown, joined our crew, we wouldn't have been in this predicament.

We had about a minute until the storm overtook our vessel. On the other side of the ship, a narrow strip of sea separated us from a jagged wall of rock along a cliffside. Several bits of stone stabbed diagonally outward from the water like defensive spears.

The weight of the storm would send us crashing into the stone, causing us to sink.

Something inside me clicked, like gears snapping into place. My mental phantom vanished as my subconscious took control.

"All paws on deck!" I shouted. I turned to Leo, who stood beside me.

"Man the helm." Then I faced Alex. "Alex, you serve as second mate. Work with Leo and pass along his orders to the crew."

"Where are you going?" he asked.

"I'm taking an oar."

We needed our fastest rowers. If we didn't fight hard enough against the waves, all would be lost.

"Everyone else, team up in threes and then grab an oar! We'll need to row for our lives. If we crash, it's over. Rowing will be difficult, much harder than during calmer waters, but we'll need to row as fast as possible. When you're tired, tag in your rowing mate. Keep switching until we get through this. Let's move!"

The incoming storm left no time to argue. Everyone hurried to their positions. I grabbed the front-most oar on the starboard side where the menacing land threatened our lives.

Rico came rushing down the center and began tossing leather gloves to all the critters. "Put these on, mates! These'll protect yer paws!"

I caught the gloves as Rico tossed them to me, slipped them on, and started rowing.

The storm hit us like a boulder hitting a wooden wall. Nearly horizontal rain pelted us, a hive of bees stinging us relentlessly from whiskers to tail. The ship began rising and falling over the turbulent waters, making it hard to remain seated on the bench behind the oar. As the ship swayed, I clutched onto the oar with all my strength, desperate to hold my place and keep rowing.

Monstrous thunder shook our bones; lightning electrified the air.

When we reached a brief reprieve from the waves, I looked to the side and saw we were still approaching land.

"Keep rowing!" I shouted. "Faster!"

I heard some moans from the crew. It sounded like Collin shouted something back in disagreement, but I couldn't understand him. I just kept rowing.

"The food!" I heard Lilly shout.

I looked over and watched in horror as a wooden crate of food smashed into the rail along the side of the ship and busted open. Someone had forgotten to secure the crate to the mast. What little remained of our food supplies emptied out into the sea.

"Keep rowing!" I repeated. We needed to stay focused on keeping the ship afloat.

We continued rowing as furiously as we could. Up, forward, down, back. Up, forward, down, back. I kept repeating those words as I moved the oar. I couldn't do another hundred strokes, but I could go up one more time. Then forward, then down, then back, and then repeat.

"Want me to fill in?" Melvin asked beside me.

"Not yet," I said, my adrenaline keeping me energized. For the time being.

We all kept rowing as fast as we could. We'd make some progress, putting distance between us and the sharp rocks, but then several waves would lash us, shredding our progress and sending us back towards a watery disaster. The pain and soreness in my muscles no longer existed: I operated on pure adrenaline.

My body trembled under another crackle of thunder, and then several gallons of seawater blasted me from the side, drenching my entire body.

I spit out a mouthful of the salty loam, wiped my eyes clean, and kept rowing.

Up, forward, down, back. Up, forward, down, back.

The waves were unrelenting. One of the critters behind me threw up over the rails as the ship heaved higher and lower with the sea. I allowed myself a second to glance back: mice still manned all the oars. That's all that mattered right now.

A chill raced through my body when the ship suddenly shook; wood splintered below deck. We'd hit something.

"Take the oar!" I shouted to Melvin beside me. He grabbed it without question, and I leapt off the bench and rushed towards Alex, who was heading down from the helm to meet me.

A large wave crashed into the side of the ship, spraying us with water and knocking me off my feet. I slid across the slippery deck and slammed into the rail on the side of the ship. For a moment, I thought the wood would snap and spit me out into the raging waters, but it held.

Recovering quickly, I rushed to meet Alex.

"What was that?" I asked.

"I didn't see anything," he said. "We must've hit one of those smaller rocks."

"Let's check it out," I said, and we rushed below deck to check for damage. We quickly found a horizontal tear in the side of the ship. Thankfully, the tear was above the base water level, although under the ferocity of the sea, water still rushed in. Several inches had already accumulated over the floorboards.

"The wood!" I shouted, pointing to a stack of wooden planks we kept for this exact purpose. The two of us grabbed a plank and threw it up to cover the tear. Leaving Alex to hold it in place, I rushed to the tool bench, rummaged through the boxes to find a hammer and nails, and raced back to quickly secure the plank in place. Lacking perfection, it would at least prevent most of the water from rushing in.

Sounds of more wood snapping and breaking assaulted our ears as another rock punctured the ship's starboard side. We both turned to the new tear, watching pieces of wood falling to the ground along with several buckets of water. Alex and I worked together to nail two planks along the wall, securing the tear the best we could.

"We can't keep this up," Alex said, taking a breath. "And if there's a tear below water, I don't think these will hold."

"I know," I said. "Let's head back up. I'm going to talk to Leo. Grab a crewmate and stay below deck to patch any more holes."

"Aye," he said.

We both raced back to the upper deck. The storm raged furiously with no end in sight as I rushed to the helm where Leo struggled to hold the wheel steady under the strong winds.

"Captain!" he said, using all his might to keep her steady. "What's the status below deck?"

"Two holes, both patched and above sea level. We can't take much more. Any ideas?"

"Look up ahead," he said, motioning to the spyglass tied to the helm. "Starboard side, about two hundred yards."

I grabbed the spyglass and gazed out. Relief swept through me as I saw the land broke up ahead, giving way to more open ocean. If we could just make it until we cleared this strip of stone and strife, we'd be out of the immediate danger from the rocks. We'd still need to withstand the storm, but at least we wouldn't be so close to the jagged perils that currently threatened us.

I set the spyglass back and raced down to the critters manning the oars.

"There's a break in the land about two hundred yards ahead!" I yelled over the din of the storm. "If we can just make it there, we'll get a reprieve. Row! Row as hard as you can!"

One of the crew looked on the verge of collapsing. I rushed towards him, tagged him out, and rowed with everything I had.

Up, forward, down, back. Up, forward, down, back.

Another crash below deck as another rock punctured us. I relied on Alex (thankfully a rower) to deal with it. We needed to keep going.

One hundred yards away.

"Almost there!" I shouted.

Up, forward, down, back. Up, forward, down, back.

Waves continuously blasted us from the side, water spraying over the deck, drenching us and nearly pushing us overboard. But we kept going. We kept going.

Finally, we cleared the treacherous rocks and the cliffs they defended. The land quickly receded as we moved forward, giving us plenty of room to drift without concern.

No longer in immediate danger, I swapped out with another crew and went to check on Alex below deck. All three tears were above sea level and properly patched.

Somehow, by the tips of our whiskers, we'd overcome our most difficult obstacle to date. Whether by grace, luck, or sheer force of will, we'd narrowly avoided catastrophe.

The storm lasted a couple hours, gradually losing intensity as time went on. By the time it stopped, all the critters had collapsed where they stood, lying on their backs, panting as they gazed up into the grey sky above.

# 13

We had barely survived the storm. We lost all our food. Probably other things as well. An already hungry crew, completely exhausted and overworked, now needed to make it another two days before reaching the next port.

The crew barely spoke the next morning as we assessed the damage, removed the remaining water from below deck, and set up a new work schedule based on everyone's condition. Some had minor injuries, such as a sprained wrist or ankle, and some had bigger ones, such as Oscar, who had a welt the size of a fist on his head from where an oar had smashed into him.

Morale couldn't get any lower. But at least we hadn't sunk.

I walked around the deck, stiff and exhausted, a shell of a mouse simply going through the motions. My lower back muscles reprimanded me every step I took, trying to force me to lie down and rest. There were so many problems, so many issues with the ship and crew. I probably needed to have one-on-ones with everyone and then solve all the new issues that sprouted up from those one-on-ones.

Alex approached me and asked to talk in my cabin. Good, a break from deciding what to do. Alex wanted to talk to me, so I'd go along.

We entered my cabin, partly illuminated under the rising sun, and sat opposite one another at my desk. Looking nervous, he gazed down at his paws folded in his lap.

"What is it?" I asked, sensing something was wrong.

"Umm…" he said, searching for words. I remained silent, giving him space. "This is hard for me to say, but I wanted to tell you that I'll be leaving when we reach Mistwood."

A lump formed in my throat. I wanted to object, to say something, but words remained just out of reach.

"I like you a lot," he continued. "I've sailed under a few different captains, and you are one of the most humble and genuine. I just can't handle the crew anymore. Every critter is so negative, and most have very little work ethic and aren't happy being here. Cooking is my passion, but because I'm one of the only crew who works hard, I'm stuck manning the oars more than anyone. I understand that keeping the ship on schedule is most important, but it's just not fair."

He spoke quickly without taking a breath. As he continued, he sounded more and more exhausted, refusing to let himself breathe until he got everything out.

"This storm could've been avoided if the crew would've kept on schedule. The food wouldn't have been lost if the crew hadn't forgotten to strap it down. There are so many other issues we deal with because not everyone is pulling their weight. It's been getting worse ever since we left Cherrystone, and I just can't take it anymore."

He finally allowed himself to pause. Both of us sat there in silence. His every word stung, though they all rang true. I couldn't blame him for leaving; I'd probably do the same.

Why was managing others so hard?

When my dad opened his nuts and seed shop, all his time got sucked into management issues. I understood it now. Without being able to properly build and motivate a team, accomplishing anything proved practically impossible.

"I wanted to tell you now," he said, "rather than waiting until we reached Mistwood. I'm sorry, Martin. I know this isn't what you wanted to hear."

I coughed to clear the sadness from my throat. "You're right, it's not, but I understand. You have every right to feel the way you do. I… honestly, I have no idea how to fix things, and I don't expect you to deal with it while I figure it out. Thank you for telling me and thank you so much for everything you've done for this voyage so far." I smiled. "It truly has been a pleasure getting to know you. I hope we stay in touch."

Alex smiled. "Of course! Thank you for taking this so well. I was really nervous to bring this up. Most captains would've blown up on me, but I can tell you genuinely care. Thank you, Martin."

We spoke a little while longer, somehow managing to laugh at some of the fond memories we shared during our voyage. Alex was such a good mouse, a good friend. I already missed him.

After our conversation, I kept to myself until we reached Mistwood. Everyone could sense my sadness and thankfully spared me a bit of complaining, aside from a comment here or there regarding the lack of food. Leo tried to cheer me up during our nightly talks. Pep talks didn't help much anymore, but our nightly games of The Eagle in the Mountains provided at least some escape.

As we pulled into the marina of Mistwood, I gazed at the dense fog that cascaded down from the mountains serving as a backdrop of the village. Tall pine trees poked out from the fog along the mountains and speckled the seaside village. In previous ports, as we drew close to the pier, we could hear the hustle and bustle of critters moving about. But here: silence. No vessels nearby. The only sound I heard was the water parting in front of our ship as we glided towards the docks.

A couple of chipmunks working as dockhands helped us secure the *Skimmer* to the pier and set up the gangway. Without much discussion, the crew quickly exited the ship, eager to find a grub spot to fill their bellies. Leo and I were the last ones off.

We walked slowly and quietly down the dock towards the Guild Hall. The sun hadn't risen yet, so most of the shops were closed. I imagined no one would be at the Guild Hall this early, but, despite not eating for a couple days, the only thing I wanted to do was go there and wait. I couldn't think of anything other than hopefully recruiting some rowers, though with Leo being our only rower currently, the outlook was grim.

At some point during our walk, Leo stopped. My spinning thoughts consumed me so much that I didn't notice until I was several paces ahead. After stopping, I walked back to him. He looked sad, like a weathered statue about to collapse. He rested on his walking stick, staring longingly at the scattered pine needles over the damp soil.

"Martin," he said.

"Yes?"

He breathed out slowly, then looked up at me.

"I really, really hate to do this. In my age and condition, I don't feel safe going to Enya without a stable crew. My heart hurts saying this, but... I'm going to have to leave."

A gentle breeze rolled over us, the morning dew sticking to our fur, keeping us cool. No critters nearby. Just the two of us.

It was over. How could I go on without Leo? I relied on him every step of the way, and now he was leaving me like this. Right when I needed him the most. How could he do this to me? Did he understand he'd just doomed my voyage, doomed... Ella?

I knew his peg leg would be an issue as soon as I saw him. I should've found a replacement before we left Cherrystone, someone more reliable. Someone I could count on.

No—it wasn't his fault. It was mine. My eyes pulsed with rage, making it difficult to see. Everything turned red, the entire world a sinker determined to drag me down as far as possible. I wanted to yell. To scream. To cry. To break something. I'd given *everything* to this voyage, everything I had, every ounce of energy, and this was the result. I couldn't blame Leo. I couldn't blame Alex or Alyssa or anyone. Deep down, I knew it was my fault, but it was too much to bear.

What should I have done? Cry? Yell? Take the high road and tell him I understood and everything would be okay when we both knew that wasn't true?

Tears streamed from my eyes. The inside of my mouth swelled with grief and frustration, making it hard to breathe, hard to speak.

I wouldn't be able to contain myself much longer. I had fought to maintain my composure despite all the blows I'd endured, but now I was about to implode. No—I *was* imploding.

Unable to form words, I turned around and ran. A coward, unable to face a challenge. But I didn't care.

I ran as fast as I could. I coughed to clear my throat but choked instead on the sobs that ripped from my chest. I cried. Hard. A flame burned inside my chest; I sputtered and gasped for air as my lungs worked in overdrive to propel my legs to run faster. I needed to get away. I needed to escape.

To run faster, I dropped to all fours, racing across the damp black soil, my face piercing new veils of mist as I leapt forward. A couple critters stepped out of their shelters, ready to start the day. I rushed past them without incident, accelerating even faster.

Reaching the end of the main street, I turned, and a few minutes later, I left the village and plunged into the surrounding pine forest. Massive pine trees towered up all around me forming a dense cover. I winced as my paw landed on pinecones, crushing them into the ground as they ripped into my flesh. In an odd way, the pain felt good, like a punishment I deserved.

My heart ready to explode, I breathed deeper, swallowing as much air as I could to pump through my body, but eventually my muscles stopped working.

I collapsed to the soil littered with needles and pinecones.

My physical energy depleted, all I could do was lie there and cry. My paw dug into the soil, gripping for something but only finding dirt. I squeezed my fist, feeling the soil squish between my fingers, and then pounded the ground over and over. I cried for everything: my frustrations with Walter and Collin, Artemis for abandoning me so soon, my dad for not teaching me more about management, myself for failing Ella. My mind spiraled, finding every possible reason to feel sorry for myself. When at last I ran out of tears, I simply laid there, motionless, my mind depleted, my skin taking solace in the coolness and softness of the soil supporting me.

Time passed. I had no idea how much. My heart rate and breath gradually normalized. My face felt warm, my eyes burned from the tears, but my strength slowly returned to me. I could stand if I wanted, but I preferred stillness. I had nowhere to be. Nothing to do.

A whistling sound echoed off the trees ahead, soon joined by the soft crunching of leaf litter under paw. Some critter was walking nearby.

Bending my elbows, my paws found purchase in the soil, and I pressed down to push myself up. I propped myself up on one leg, and then both. Feeling wobbly, I stumbled to a log nearby and sat on top of it. The whistling got closer, and eventually a squirrel emerged from the mist. She saw me and casually approached, whistling all the way until she was a few paces in front of me.

This squirrel wore a cloth tunic, something like I would make in my shop, with a small green backpack strapped over her shoulders.

"Well hello there," she said in a pleasant, chipper tone. "You're up fairly early. What are you doing out here?" She motioned to all the pine needles and dirt covering my body. "You look like you got into a tumble with a chipmunk, you do. And…" she squinted, looking deep into my eyes. "Yes, oh my. You've been releasing some tears, haven't ya?"

"I'm fine," I said, brushing all the debris off my chest.

"You're fine and I'm a turkey," she said, dropping her backpack to the ground and plopping onto the log beside me. Her being three times my size, the log shook upon impact. "Name's Luna. And you are?"

I looked away from her and gazed at the ground. I wasn't in the mood for conversation. "Martin."

"Well Martin, you sir are in luck. I don't recognize you, so you must be a visitor. I'm the Mistwood sage. I was just finishing my morning hike before heading to my hut for the day. I've got a little bit of time, so why don't you tell me what's troubling ya so I can set you on the right path?"

I looked at her. "You're not a raccoon."

She grabbed her belly and let out a hearty laugh. "Well there's no trouble with yer eyesight, that's for sure! Right you are. As my tail and fur probably give away, I'm a squirrel." She leaned closer, lowering her voice to a whisper and putting her paw around her mouth as if about to tell a secret. "Between me, you, and these pine trees, I always thought squirrels were better sages than raccoons."

She chuckled playfully and sat back up.

"Come, come," she said. "Let's hear it."

After Nibbletown, I'd decided to stop listening to sages since it didn't help. Luna seemed different than the others (aside from being an entirely different animal). She seemed more casual, humbler...like she genuinely cared. Her demeanor invited me to confide in her, so I did. I explained everything, every single detail. I didn't hold anything back. Despite my best intentions, I even revealed my anger at everyone: my crew, the other sages, myself. I honestly didn't care if I offended her and made her leave. I was done hiding my feelings. I put everything out in the open.

Upon my finishing, Luna casually slipped one of her foot paws through a loop around her backpack and pulled it closer. She unzipped it and pulled out two large gooseberries, handed one to me, and bit into the other. What was it with sages and eating or drinking? I followed her lead and sampled mine, enjoying the sweet and sour fruit as it wakened my tastebuds.

"Thank you for being so open with me," she said, swallowing a bite. "Most critters hold back a little, not wanting to make themselves vulnerable or not quite trusting me. Which is understandable, but it makes it hard to give good feedback."

She took another bite, gazing off into the blanket of fog that drifted gently between the trees. I found myself surprisingly at ease, at some semblance of peace. After crying and running and venting, it felt good to just be still in the quiet forest.

"Where to begin," she said, giving herself a few long moments to think. "Okay, so first, much of what you've been told is wrong. Well, maybe not completely wrong, but mostly wrong."

A small wave of relief washed through me. I expected Luna to repeat the same advice the other sages gave, only in more detail. Hearing she had an entirely different perspective gave me hope.

"Firstly, motivating critters is a waste of time. It's far better to find self-motivated critters and then fight like heck to make sure you don't demotivate them. It sounds like the critters you describe as rowers fit the description of self-motivated critters.

"Secondly, you've been spending your time in completely the reverse order. You should spend most of your time with the rowers. If any time is left over, you may spend it with the watchers. And if any time is left after that—well, in that case, you're probably forgetting to focus on other things—but *then* you may spend it with the sinkers.

"By putting all your energy towards the sinkers and then watchers, you've left the rowers, your self-motivated critters, feeling neglected. They're working the hardest and are the most passionate about the team's success, and yet they get the least amount of your time. Instead, those who aren't pulling their weight get all your attention. How's that fair?"

She paused for a second, letting me process everything she said before continuing.

"By keeping the sinkers on board and not firing them, you're further demotivating the rowers. Imagine I'm on your crew and I work my tail off, but everyone else barely puts any effort in and receives no consequences. What's my incentive to work hard? I'll either stop working so hard, causing what you experienced with rowers changing to sinkers, or I'll leave and go find a leader who values my hard work."

"But if I just fire critters for being sinkers, that seems cold," I said. "Is that fair to them?"

"No critter likes being fired," Luna said. "But let me challenge your perspective. I agree with the previous sages when they said that critters aren't inherently rowers or sinkers: they are rowers or sinkers in particular environments. If I hate cooking and you give me a job as a chef, I'll probably be considered a sinker. If I love foraging and you hire me to forage berries for the market, I'll be considered one of the best rowers.

"Critters can even be rowers or sinkers in the same type of work but with different cultures. If I like strict discipline and detailed orders to follow, I'll be a rower if you are a manager who gives specific instructions but a sinker if you leave it to the crew to take their own initiative.

"If a critter is a sinker, it's due to one of three things: they lack the knowledge, training, or tools to do the job; they aren't a good fit for the type of work; or they aren't a good fit for the type of culture. If you notice a critter is a sinker, your first goal is to ensure they have the knowledge, training, and tools to do the job and you aren't doing anything that is discouraging them.

"If they don't enjoy the type of work, or they don't enjoy the culture and you don't want to change it, they will never enjoy working for you and you'll never enjoy working with them. By keeping them on the team at that point, you're wasting your time and, what most don't realize, you're also wasting *their* time. Every day a crewmate stays with you when he clearly isn't a good fit is a day you're robbing him from finding some other work that resonates with his passions. It's not fair to him to keep him longer than you should."

Thoughts whizzed through my head. Finally, the pieces were coming together. Managing this way sounded significantly more enjoyable than spending all my time with sinkers.

"How do I know when I should fire a sinker? I want to make sure I'm not being too hasty and unfair."

"Honesty and transparency," Luna said. "If someone isn't cutting it, as quickly as possible, have a chat with him. Say something like: 'So, I want to be upfront and honest with you about something. I could be wrong, so I'd like to share my perspective and get your thoughts. From my point of view, you aren't pulling your weight because of this and that. Do you agree or disagree?'

"If they don't agree, you simply need to explain your expectations and show specifically how they aren't meeting them. If they do agree, ask if there's anything you can do to help them succeed, or if there's anything you're doing or not doing that's holding them back. Ask if you can provide any resources or tools or training to help. Keep talking until you've explored all possibilities and addressed all concerns and questions. Then—and this is the step most miss—it's imperative you summarize what you both agreed upon *and what the consequence will be if things don't improve.*

"Because that last step is usually uncomfortable, most leaders either skip it entirely or mitigate the message so much it's lost. You owe it to the other critter to be crisp and clear. Say something like, 'We agreed that I would do this and that for you, and in exchange, you will do this and that while working. We'll meet up again in two weeks. If things haven't improved, then I'll have to give you a final warning, and if things still don't improve in another two weeks, we'll need to go our separate ways. Do you agree with all that, and does any of that sound unfair to you?'

"Once you've finalized the conversation, you both are crystal clear with the expectations and consequences. At this point, either things will improve quickly, or, more likely, the critter will end up quitting before it escalates to them being fired. This is far preferable to the sinkers hanging around spreading toxicity and dragging down your team until, after enough complaining and procrastination, you finally fire them."

"What if I fire sinkers so quickly but can't find any rowers to take their place? I'll either be replacing sinkers with sinkers or leaving the rowers short-staffed."

"It's usually better to be short-staffed with a team of rowers than fully staffed with sinkers," Luna said. "Since rowers typically need to make up for sinkers, rowers work nearly as hard whether short-staffed or on a team with sinkers. Even if you lost so many sinkers that your team physically couldn't move forward as much without them, this setback would only be temporary. Your positive culture would eventually attract other rowers, and then your team would be far more productive.

"So it's a short-term pain for a long-term gain. If instead you kept the sinkers to avoid being short-staffed, the rowers would gradually leave, and you'd be in a far worse spot long-term."

A mental quill feverishly scribbled all these notes and filed them away in my mind, hopefully for me to recall later when I got back to my crew. This all made so much sense. Motivating critters drained so much of my energy, and the effects were almost always temporary. It was a never-ending cycle. Instead, getting a crew of self-motivated critters and then simply making sure I didn't demotivate them sounded a lot easier and more rewarding for everyone.

I sat with Luna for a while more, picking her brain, thinking of all the difficult decisions and conversations I'd encountered during the voyage and asking her advice. She spoke so fluently, so smoothly, and everything she said brought such clarity.

At the end, when I had no further questions, she asked, "Why did you follow the advice from the other sages if it didn't sit well with you?"

I shrugged. "I don't know. I know nothing of leadership, and they're supposed to be experts. I just trusted them."

She smiled softly. "There are a lot of critters out there with fancy titles, supposed experts in the field. When you hear advice, if it doesn't resonate with your core, there's likely a reason. Trust your instinct, that initial flash of feeling you get when hearing advice from others. If it doesn't sit well with you, either don't follow it or challenge it until it clicks. There are multiple ways of accomplishing most things in life. If you're trying to use a technique that doesn't agree with who you are, it won't work."

"Thank you," I said. "That makes perfect sense."

While I understood her points and had more clarity, was I too late? With Leo leaving, did I have enough time to put her advice to use and still make it back in time to save Ella?

We finished the conversation, said our farewells, and then I stood up and headed back for the village.

I needed to change things, and I needed to do it now. It was do or die, and with Ella's life on the line, I couldn't fail. If Leo and Alex left now, this voyage would be lost. I didn't have the luxury to think about what Luna said, plan what I should do, get other critters' opinions, and slowly make changes.

No. I needed to make drastic changes immediately. By acting quickly without taking the time to fully plan everything, I may make some mistakes, but those mistakes would be minor compared to taking too long to act.

I could do this. I knew it in my heart, and I couldn't help but smile.

# 14

"Leo!" I shouted as I saw him walking down the street between shops. The sun had illuminated the thin fog a soothing white.

He looked up at me, just as solemn as I'd left him. His face formed a puzzled expression as he saw me rushing towards him, full of energy, the complete opposite of the Martin he'd seen running away in tears just an hour prior.

"Leo," I repeated as I stopped next to him, giving myself a second to catch my breath. "I understand what I've been doing wrong. I get it now."

"You get what?"

"How to lead," I said. "I know why the crew got to the point it's at now. It's been completely my fault, and I know how to fix it."

Some hope snuck into his voice. "How's that? What happened to you?"

"I spoke with Luna, the local sage. She explained everything. Much of what the previous sages told me was wrong. Not only wrong, but backwards. I know I can do this, Leo. Please, will you give me one more chance? I promise if you don't see large improvements by the next port, I'll kick you off the *Skimmer* myself."

He chuckled. "I've never seen you like this, Martin. What are you going to do differently?"

"Let me show you."

I had Leo save us a few tables at one of the pubs while I rushed around town to find my crew. When I spotted Alex, I told him I would be completely changing the culture going forward. I pleaded for him to attend this one final meeting before deciding to leave, and thankfully, he agreed.

After finding everyone, I gathered them to the pub, got everyone seated at a table with a mug of cold apple cordial—a little something to put them in a good mood—and then addressed them.

"Everyone," I said. "I have not been the best captain on this voyage. In fact, I've been pretty bad. During our journey, some critters have been working passionately, trying to help us successfully complete our mission. Others have been complaining, finding excuses not to work, and dragging others down.

"Unfortunately, I've spent most of my time with the latter. This has resulted in me not spending time with those working the hardest."

I motioned with my paw towards Oscar.

"Oscar, I am sorry for pushing off our meetings at the beginning of the voyage to hear your fishing ideas. That wasn't fair to you, and it cost the entire crew hearty meals when our food supply got low. I am truly sorry."

I gave a couple more examples of rowers I had neglected in the past and how it caused them to leave the crew, and then moved on to my plan.

"Going forward, I'm not going to try and motivate any of you. If you don't want to be here, then please leave. If you want to be on the crew but aren't happy with how I've been running things, please talk to me. And when we do talk, please be honest and transparent. Don't mitigate what you're trying to say to avoid hurting my feelings. Going forward, my number one priority is making sure I'm supporting those of you who genuinely want to be here."

I scanned my crew. Several of them, such as Oscar, Alex, and Melvin, nodded their heads in agreement. Others, like Walter and Collin, seemed on edge. That was fine. My priorities no longer included making everyone happy.

"So basically," Collin said, "you're telling us you're done trying to make things better and just want us to work hard without complaining?" He looked around, seeking nods of agreements from his crewmates.

"No," Oscar said, "that's not what he said at all. He said if you have genuine concerns, he's happy to hear them, but he's not going to continue wasting time trying to motivate those who don't want to be motivated."

"What gives you the right to decide who works hard and who doesn't?" Walter challenged.

"We will all review our current work schedule and discuss any changes," I said. "If anyone thinks our schedule is unfair or unreasonable, please feel free to share those concerns so we can all agree collectively on what's expected. If you want more breaks, be prepared to show us how we can allocate more breaks while still completing our mission. If you want longer shifts, shorter shifts, or whatever you want, we'll listen to all opinions.

"It's possible we may not be able to accommodate everyone's wishes, but we'll do the best we can. Once we've agreed upon the schedule and the expectations of each critter, everyone will be held to the same standard, including myself. If we need to change those standards during the voyage, no problem, just let me know. We'll evaluate those standards as a team as often as needed. Once those agreements are made and we've ensured everyone knows and understands the expectations, any critter repeatedly not following them without valid reason will be cut from the crew."

"What if we don't all agree on the expectations?" Walter asked.

"I'm sure we won't," I said. "But we'll try our best. We all need to accept that things might not perfectly align with each critter's individual wants, but all opinions will be heard and considered. Hopefully, you trust Leo's and my judgement on issues where opinions differ. If you don't, then you should ask yourself if you'd be happier working for a different captain. I am not trying to sound harsh; I'm just trying to be honest and up front with everyone.

"I'd love nothing more than for all of us to work together to reach Enya in time, but I do understand that my leadership style or the workload won't resonate with everyone. And that's perfectly okay. That doesn't mean anything is necessarily wrong with you or me; we just aren't a good fit and will be happier going our separate ways."

Collin stood up, scooting his stool loudly across the floor. "I'm sorry guys, but I'm not going to work for a captain who's just going to fire us because we don't dance to his tune. If we aren't meeting his standards,

he should work with us until we do. Everyone is capable of being successful. No one should be fired because the captain is too lazy to work
with them."

"Again," Alex said, "he's not saying that at all. He's simply saying—
"

"It's fine," I interrupted. Collin's demeanor clearly indicated he didn't
want to stay. Better to rip the sap off now and move on. "Let him go.
Collin, I hope you find a captain who better serves your needs."

He scoffed, not expecting me to let him go so easily. With nothing
left to say, he stormed off and exited the pub. After some back and forth,
three other critters left. I was surprised Walter stayed; part of me wished
he'd go. Although who knew, maybe with this new culture, he'd thrive.
My prior management style could've been holding him back.

After I addressed all the questions and concerns, we as a team looked
over the schedule and discussed desired changes. We then discussed and
agreed upon expectations for each critter during their shifts. Finally, we
agreed on what actions the crew thought were appropriate for critters
who weren't pulling their weight. We came to near unanimous agreement on almost everything. Because this process was so collaborative,
the critters were very open-minded and agreeable to things even if they
didn't always get their way.

Finally, when we completed all the discussions and understood the
workload, expectations, and consequences (good and bad), we remained
gathered in silence for a few moments, letting everything sink in.

"Okay," I said, gathering the papers that captured all our agreements.
"Let's head to the Guild Hall. I'm going to need your help to recruit

critters with the best talents and passion. They will want to work for a crew with a positive culture. Even though things have been rough in the past, hopefully you feel good about where we're heading. Please share this with as many critters as you can to help Leo and I recruit and let us know if you find a critter you think would be a great fit. We'd love your input on the crew going forward."

Several of the crew smiled and nodded, a few murmured agreements.

"Let's do this!" Alex said, slamming his mug on the table.

The rest of the crew agreed, and we all headed to the Guild Hall for the first time as a unified team.

# 15

That was our most successful trip to the Guild Hall. With my crew helping, we managed to recruit two watchers and a rower! Replacing the three sinkers left us with three rowers, ten watchers, and eight sinkers. Far from ideal, but better. I also suspected some current sinkers, such as Oscar, would rise to be rowers under the new culture.

One of the newest rowers, a fuzzy tan gerbil with specks of dark-brown fur named Harry, was an herbalist. Once he got started talking about various herbs and spices, stopping him proved a challenge. He brought a selection of potions, some that reduced seasickness and others that provided energy. He also had all sorts of salves and bandages to cure wounds and prevent infections. He proved a welcome addition to the team.

Before we left, I finally pulled Oscar aside to hear his thoughts on fishing. He took me to one of the local vendors that sold fishing equipment and explained two different fishing techniques: trolling and trawling. Trolling involved buying pole mounts to fasten to the deck rails so several rods could be utilized at once by a single crewmate. Trawling involved fastening a net to the stern of the ship and pulling it through the water as the ship moved forward, catching anything in its path.

Originally, I had avoided purchasing any superfluous fishing gear given our tight budget. Oscar explained the extra fish we'd catch would reduce the need to spend as much on food supplies, thus paying for itself.

Trusting him, I purchased some extra fishing rods, mounts, and a net. Then I put him in charge of implementing everything, which delighted him.

We all boarded the *Skimmer* and set out. After a short while, we slipped out of the fog surrounding Mistwood and gazed upon the open sea to the north. I watched Oscar work excitedly with Rico to set up the new fishing equipment. Oscar did this all without a checklist or any directive from me. He just did. I loved it.

"Captain," Walter said, stepping up beside me on the deck. "I need to talk with you."

Given the productiveness of my conversation with Oscar, talking with the other rowers seemed a better use of my time. And more enjoyable. However, none of them specifically asked to talk to me like Walter. I'd just talk with Walter and anyone else who needed me, and then I'd—

No. I needed to set my own priorities rather than letting others set them for me. Otherwise, I'd spend all my time chatting with those who requested it and be left hoping for time with the rowers. Instead, I'd follow Luna's advice and talk to the rowers first and then speak with as many other critters as time allowed.

"I need to talk with a few others first," I told Walter. "I'll come find you later when I'm free."

"But I need to talk to you now," he said.

"What's it about?"

"The crew and I have some concerns over the new schedule."

So nothing urgent.

"It'll have to wait," I said. "I have others I need to speak with first. I'll come find you later."

I spotted Alex up on deck, approached him, and invited him to chat. Rather than retreating to my cabin as in the past, we found a sunny spot on deck and sat on two supply crates. Since our conversation would be more positive in nature, privacy wasn't necessary.

Keeping Luna's advice in mind, after we exchanged pleasantries, I got to the point.

"Alex, you've been a pleasure to have on board since day one. We haven't spoken much, so I just wanted to pull you aside to see if there was anything I was or was not doing that was bothering you, or if there was anything I could do to make you feel more empowered."

"What do you mean by empowered?" he asked.

"Well, I don't want you just feeling like a number here following orders. You are smart and passionate, so I want you feeling comfortable sharing any ideas or suggestions on how to improve things."

"Hmm..." he said, gazing slightly up to the sky, fishing through his thoughts for ideas. "No captain has ever asked me for my opinion like this. This feels rather nice."

I smiled and we both laughed a little. "Good," I said. "I'm glad."

"I've never really thought about things like this," he said. "I'll need some time to consider it. Although there is one thing. I'm sure this won't work because the rest of the crew would probably think it unfair. But as you know, my passion is cooking. I'd absolutely love it if I could be on kitchen duty fulltime. With short shifts in the kitchen, it's hard to really get things set up, get enough practice to learn everyone's food preferences, and create great meals. But if that was my sole focus, I could really elevate the food."

"That sounds like a great idea," I said. "What makes you think the rest will think it's unfair?"

Alex shrugged. "Most will probably think I'm just trying to get out of rowing duty."

"I see your point," I said. Most considered rowing the worst shift, and most of the sinkers constantly came up with excuses to get out of it. "Tell you what, I'll touch base with everyone and see if anyone has any objections to trying it out for a couple days. They can try your cooking and see the difference when you're able to devote all your energy towards it, and then we can touch base to see how everyone feels. How does that sound?"

"That sounds great," Alex said, smiling. His gaze shifted to the side as he envisioned himself in his new position. "That would be so much fun, cooking all the time." He looked back at me. "Please let me know what they say!"

"I will."

We chatted a bit more, and then I sent him on his way and met up with Harry. I spoke with Harry for a while and listened as he explained the different potions he currently had and ones he could make if we got certain supplies at the next port. He was most excited about an apple cordial he made with ginger root, cinnamon, cayenne, and tea leaves. He let me try a sip, and it tasted delicious: a burst of sweetness with a kick of heat. He claimed it provided a midday energy boost, best drunk shortly after the noon sun.

Energy or no energy, it tasted great, so when he offered to make a drink for everyone after lunch, I approved.

After encouraging him to let me know if I could do anything to make improvements or if he had any suggestions for the voyage, we parted ways, and I found Leo. I shared my conversations with Oscar, Alex, and Harry, and the new ideas we had generated. Leo smiled as I spoke, asking questions here or there, but mainly just enjoying the conversation.

"I have to say," he said after I finished, "it's only been a few hours since we left Mistwood, but I can already notice a change around here. Especially in you. You're like an entirely different captain."

"I feel *so* good," I said. "Working this way feels so much more natural. So much easier. And I'm happier. Everyone I talk to is happier. Most importantly, it's leading to results. If all goes well, we'll have more fish to eat, better food with Alex's cooking, and tasty afternoon cordials. That's only from talking to three critters. Imagine if all twenty-one crewmates acted like that."

A glimpse of Walter out of the corner of my eye dampened my excitement. He seemed angrier than ever, a dark storm cloud in an otherwise cloudless sky. The sight of me laughing and being so excited probably didn't help. I needed to talk with him now to get a clear mind before I approached the rest of the crew.

Unfortunately, this would be a below-deck conversation.

# 16

"Yes?" I asked Walter, both of us seated at my desk.

"This has to stop."

"What does?"

"Your attitude. Firing anyone you think is lazy."

"That's not what I'm doing."

"That's how you're coming across."

"What makes you say that?"

Walter glared at me, then evaded the question and moved on. "The crew have several concerns."

"Such as what?"

"They aren't happy with the new schedule."

"Why didn't they say anything when we came up with it as a group?"

"Because they didn't feel comfortable."

"Okay," I said. "What changes would they like made that still allow us to successfully complete our voyage?"

"They don't know. All they know is the current schedule isn't working."

My fingers wandered along my smooth wooden desk as I searched for the right words. "Well, I'm open to changes. But if they don't have any ideas, it's hard for me to take much action."

"It's your job as the captain to figure it out."

"From my perspective, there's nothing to figure out. You keep bringing up supposed concerns the crew has, but no one ever brings them to my attention, even when I have a meeting with them and ask."

"That's because they don't feel comfortable—"

"Then I can't help them," I said, growing frustrated. "I need a crew who can communicate with me. These crewmates you've been speaking of since we started this voyage seem to have concerns they only voice to you. They never have any solutions, and they refuse to communicate with me directly. That's simply not a healthy working relationship. I'm happy to listen to concerns anyone has and brainstorm solutions. But if they don't feel comfortable communicating with me, then I'm probably not the right captain for them."

"See," Walter said, stomping his paw on the wooden floorboards. "There you go again, blaming the crew and stating they should be fired because they don't work the way you want them to."

"Walter, I'm not saying that. If they don't feel comfortable communicating with me, and it's not due to anything I've done, then I'll never be able to solve their issues. Either they can remain on the crew and be miserable, or they can find a different captain they deem more approachable and make us both better off."

Walter kept pushing back, finding new reasons to disagree with me or tell me I was wrong. The more he spoke, the more I doubted any of the crew actually had these issues. Every minute I remained in this discussion drained time that could be used more productively.

After a while, my patience emptied, I said. "Walter, look. We're talking in circles at this point. I am very motivated and focused on improving the culture and environment here, and I'm already seeing positive changes. I need to prioritize my time focusing on improvements, not blindly chasing concerns. I don't mean this in any negative way, but this is who I am and how I want to lead. If you don't like the culture I'm creating and how I'm choosing to spend my time, we may not be suited to be on the same crew."

"Are you firing me?" he asked, his face tightening.

"No, I'm just sharing my feelings."

An awkward pause sat between us until I stood up.

"Unless there's anything else, I need to do a few things on deck."

Walter reluctantly stood. Clearly unsatisfied but unable to think of anything else to say, he quietly sauntered out of the room. As soon as the door closed behind him, I leaned against my desk, propping myself up with both paws, and breathed out. I didn't like conflict—in fact, I hated it. But it felt good putting a stop to the conversation. Previously, this conversation would've soaked up an hour of my time, if not more, leaving me mentally exhausted. Now, I made it out in ten minutes with only a few minor scuffs, still full of energy.

I went up on deck and spent the rest of the afternoon chatting with the crew and helping with various projects. As time passed, more and more of the crew approached me. Previously, whenever a critter started a conversation, negativity prevailed. Now, nearly every conversation centered around a new idea or some other productive topic.

Several of the sinkers became watchers, and even a couple watchers, such as Melvin, became rowers. For the first time ever, we stayed on track as we sailed towards the next port. Too early to tell, but it seemed we were actually gaining time, which was a nice surprise.

The entire crew, except for Walter, approved of Alex's new role as the full-time chef. That little rodent bounced around with so much energy I thought he would pop off the side of the ship. The influx of fresh fish from Oscar's fishing system provided him ample ingredients with which to experiment. Nearly every thirty minutes, Alex raced around the ship giving everyone little samples of his latest creation and asked for their feedback. He learned who liked spicy food, who preferred mild, what veggies and grains each critter liked, and all the other nuances of each critter's personal palate.

The uptick in food quality and quantity further bolstered everyone's spirits, which spilled over into increased productivity.

At night, the day's good vibes flowed into my The Eagle in the Mountains games with Leo. We frequently found ourselves chatting and laughing deep into the night.

Things continued to improve over the next several days. Nearly everyone enjoyed themselves substantially more than prior to Mistwood, other than Walter and a few others. I no longer needed the monocle to identify the rowers from the sinkers. As I spent more time with the self-motivated crew, the rowers grew more energetic and sinkers more frustrated. The contrast between them practically slapped me across the face.

Early one morning, about an hour from our next port, Vale, I pulled Walter into my cabin. Butterflies fluttered inside my stomach, some rising and getting stuck in my throat, making it difficult to swallow. This would be my least favorite conversation so far.

"Yes?" Walter asked with irritation as he sat.

Ever since our initial conversation during this leg of the voyage, Walter had become embittered and withdrawn. Several crewmates told me of his unhappiness both with me and the voyage. He had been encouraging others to stop working and tried to convince them of the unreasonableness of my expectations. Fortunately, most of the crew disagreed, though he still was creating a toxic environment. Removing toxicity topped the list for ensuring rowers remained motivated.

I reflected on part of Luna's advice:

*If there is a problem with someone on the team, especially if it's infecting others, the time to act is* ***now****.*

After talking at length with Leo last night, we'd agreed on what I had to do. My nerves quivered; I had no appetite for small talk. I needed to cut to the chase.

"Walter, it's clear how unhappy you are with me as a captain and the way I'm running things. No matter how many times we talk, this keeps coming back up, and you're getting increasingly more frustrated with me. Our relationship isn't healthy for us or the others. Because of this, I am no longer keeping you on the crew once we reach Vale."

I spoke all those words without taking a breath, so I had to stop and gasp for air. He took my pause as an invitation to speak.

"This is so wrong! You know that, don't you?" He didn't wait for me to answer. "I'm one of the hardest working crew on this ship. If you would've made me your first mate like I asked, everything would've been better. We probably would've reached Enya by now."

He continued venting for several minutes while I calmly listened. His anger further validated the correctness of my decision. Finally, when he stopped, I said, "I'm sorry you feel that way. There's nothing I can say that will change your perspective, which is fine."

Given the money we'll be saving by catching our own fish and spending less on food, I had some extra room in the budget to make situations like this easier.

"I'll give you enough copper to buy a ride back to Cherrystone," I said. "Do you have any other questions for me?"

He stood up so violently that his chair fell backwards and crashed to the floor. Then he stormed out, slamming the door behind him.

I immediately felt relief, as if I had been carrying a backpack laden with stones and finally dropped it. So much of my time and energy went into Walter. Now he was gone, freeing me of a huge mental burden.

Before I could relax too much, I had two other sinkers I needed to let go. I called them in one at a time and had a conversation like that with Walter. Augusto, the first critter I spoke with, gave a couple sarcastic remarks and then left. The second, Lilly, actually agreed with me and thanked me for having the conversation. She had wanted to leave for some time to pursue her other interests but couldn't work up the courage to quit and didn't want to let me or my daughter down, so she was happy to separate amicably, especially when I offered her a small crate of Alex's cooking as a parting gift.

Though happy with my decision, my entire body shook as my nerves began to calm. I went up on deck for some fresh air and propped my folded arms on the rail at the ship's bow. Closing my eyes, I focused on the salty ocean air blowing against my face. I listened to the wind racing overtop the water, the rolling waves bumping alongside the ship, the creaking of wood as the *Skimmer* swam towards Vale. The ship herself seemed to be working harder, propelled forward by the crew's energy.

A buzzing sound pulled at my attention, and I noticed a honeybee settling down on the deck's rail. A honeybee this far off land? She must be quite the determined bee to have flown so far out over the water. Maybe she, too, was on a mission, much like me.

The honeybee rested on the rail, no doubt replenishing her stamina. If only mice could talk to insects, I'd love to hear her story. But with the language gap, I simply enjoyed being close to another critter pushing herself beyond what most think is possible.

"Everything okay, Cap'n?" Alex's voice startled me as he mimicked my stance leaning against the rail.

"Yeah," I said, gazing back out over the water. "I'm just taking a minute."

"What happened?" he asked.

"I just cut three crewmates."

"Really? Who?"

"Lilly and Augusto. Those went decently well. Lilly thanked me. I think we both realized she doesn't like working on a ship. She's excited to pursue her other passions."

"Ah, that makes sense. She seems too artistic for this type of work. I'm sure she'll find her niche somewhere in the arts."

"Yeah, I hope so," I said, watching land materialize on the horizon.

"Who was the third?"

"Hmm?" I asked, looking at Alex.

"You said you fired three critters. Lilly, Augusto, who was the third?"

"Oh," I said, looking back at the sea. "Walter."

A large exhale escaped Alex's mouth.

"Well that's a relief. What took you so long?"

# 17

Snowcapped mountains jutted up around the village of Vale. The temperature had dropped substantially since Mistwood, so I wasn't surprised when I suddenly heard Rico sneak up behind me saying, "Imagine walking around wearing *thiiis!*"

He held out a poofy green sweater that was clearly designed for comfort rather than fashion. Being a thinner mouse, I lacked proper insulation for colder climates, so as usual, I succumbed to Rico's persuasion, forked over a few coppers, and slipped the sweater over my head. The sweater's warm embrace calmed my shivering, soothing my shaking bones even if it made me look like an overripe brussels sprout.

"Thank you," I said. How did he fit so many things in his coat?

After docking, we all grabbed some breakfast and made our way to the Guild Hall. Recruiting went just as well as it had in Mistwood, if not better (no doubt Alex's decision to hand out salted crackers with some fig jam and aged cheddar contributed to our success).

First, we recruited Salva, a larger mouse with reddish-brown fur who, in addition to being a deckhand, was a skilled engineer. He brought with him a slew of little contraptions he'd designed, many of them fun gadgets that lacked any practical purpose, but others that could prove useful on our journey, like a pretty cool net launcher and slingshot.

Next was Madeline, a short, purple-furred mouse sporting a wool hat. A natural chemist, various vials and beakers clinked in her oversized rucksack as she walked, reminding me somewhat of Rico. A protective wax that sealed wood fibers topped the list of concoctions she brought to help our voyage.

Last to join, Clive was our first mole on the crew. His enlarged paws managed to delicately work his most precious item: a flute named Flu. He knew all the popular sea tunes and a slew of other energizing songs to share onboard.

The diversity of our crew finally started blooming, which provided its own source of motivation. Without my having to organize it, the crew decided to grab some lunch to welcome the three newcomers to the team. Afterwards, they headed to the supply stores to ensure we had the proper provisions for the next leg of the journey.

Leaving them to handle the supplies, I visited the local sage—another raccoon. This was a shorter visit. He explained some other tactics on how to have difficult conversations with the crew and how to determine whether a crew member needed my support or was simply not a good fit.

While talking with him, an odd concern materialized, one I hadn't experienced before.

"As the crew is becoming more talented," I said. "I'm noticing they're more knowledgeable than me in a lot of areas. Sometimes someone will ask me a question, and part of me wants to defer them to someone else instead."

"So do that," the sage replied simply.

"I'm afraid if I do that too much, I'll come across as incompetent."

"Utilizing a fellow team member wiser than you is the inverse of incompetence."

"I suppose so," I said. "I'm just trying to avoid making myself vulnerable."

"Why?"

"If I appear vulnerable, I'll appear weak. Don't critters want a strong leader?"

"Young one," he said, smiling. "Making yourself vulnerable to others is one of the strongest things you can do, leader or not. So many critters go to such length to hide their vulnerability, to hide their weaknesses. We are all vulnerable. We are all weak in certain areas. When you refuse to hide behind false confidence, others see you as a real critter, someone they can relate to. A leader who knows all the answers doesn't exist. Those who pretend they do are frauds, and their followers know it. Being strong enough to say *I don't know* to a question is a sign of strength."

That felt reassuring. After finishing the conversation with the sage, I roamed around for an hour or so, thankful to be nestled in my new sweater, and boarded the ship.

We left Vale and set out for the next port: Snowdrift.

# 18

The next leg of the journey passed without incident. Morale continued to improve as the crew bonded and learned each other's talents. Hardly anyone complained, and everyone contributed. Productivity improved so much Leo and I offered to tweak the schedule to fit in more break time, but the rest of the crew felt it unnecessary. Instead, we made use of the extra two oars to increase our speed. They wanted to make up for lost time, and the sooner we got back to Cherrystone, the sooner they could either relax or find their next job.

Between the good food, Clive's uppity tunes, Harry's tasty elixirs, and everyone's overall positive attitude, life was good aboard the *Skimmer*. A sweep of the crew with my monocle revealed twelve rowers, six watchers, and three sinkers, a significantly more pleasant mix than before.

As the temperature dropped, rowing became more challenging, but the crew pressed on. Fortunately, Rico was at the ready to sell all sorts of warm attire, from little mittens and hats to coats and paw protectors.

We sailed close enough to land for it to remain visible. The further north we traveled, the further the snow descended the mountaintops. Driftwood from dead pine trees floated along the water, effortlessly bobbing along the water's surface under the current's pull. Hardly any wildlife could be seen this far north, but fortunately, our fishing continued proving fruitful.

As I took a short break on deck, Madeline stepped up beside me and held up an opened vial and a small plank of wood.

"Check this out," she said as she held the plank as far over the side of the ship as she could. Very carefully, she tipped the vial sideways, causing a green liquid to flow close to the top. One whisker-width at a time, with intense focus, she continued tipping the vial until a few drops of the green liquid fell from the vial and splashed onto the plank. The point of impact immediately began bubbling and hissing, releasing a burning aroma. The blue of the seawater poked through a newly formed hole in the plank. The hole expanded a little more before stopping as it absorbed the liquid.

"What is that?" I asked.

"It's a new type of acid I created," she said. "It eats through wood!"

She sounded unusually excited.

"That's... great. What would we use this for?"

"Pirates!" she said. "I can make a large batch of this, and if we're ever attacked by pirates, we can use Salva's slingshot or even his net launcher to launch pouches of this to their ship and sink it!"

I laughed. "Are you expecting to see pirates this far north?"

"Just being cautious," she said with a smile, and scurried below deck to her makeshift lab.

I appreciated her imagination and effort, but hoped we'd never have to use her invention.

We continued moving north at a steady pace despite the cold. Heavy white clouds drifted across the sky above, and on the third day after leaving Vale, they finally released a curtain of puffy snowflakes that calmly descended to the sea. Within minutes, a thin layer of snow blanketed all surfaces except for the water.

The snow accompanied us for the rest of the leg and continued to fall as we pulled into the marina of Snowdrift. The trip from Snowdrift to the final port, Anchorville, would last a full week, the longest segment of the journey. As soon as we docked, everyone hurried off to secure the supplies we needed.

Snowdrift looked exactly as one would expect: a small little town with rounded roofs covered in several inches of snow. The surrounding land appeared mostly flat, void of any mountains or hills. Wood-burning fires illuminated most of the shelters from within arched windows. Their glow invited travelers to step inside and escape the cold. As I soon learned, all the shops provided freshly brewed hot tea or coffee, encouraging visitors to browse their wares and, of course, buy something.

I had let the remaining three sinkers go, so after purchasing our supplies, we headed to the Guild Hall. Recruiting at this point had become a breeze. Rather than Leo and I needing to seek out rowers and beg them to join us, the rowers noticed our team synergy and proactively approached us.

We picked up Francis, a ropemaker, Angela, a former captain with years of experience at sea, and Ismay, a former adventurer with experience specifically traveling to Enya.

"Tell me about your trip to Enya," I asked Ismay after Leo and I stepped outside with her to escape the noise. My paws instinctively folded across my chest and rubbed my arms for warmth.

"Well, it was about three seasons ago," she said, keeping her voice low so no one could overhear. "We had made it all the way to the lake that guards the entrance to Enya."

She paused a moment, reflecting on the memory. Something troubled her.

"What happened?" I asked.

"When we first entered the lake, we simply let the ship's momentum carry us forward. It was a beautiful sight. Trees were in full bloom with bright pink and purple flowers. It felt surreal. We all just took in the view for a moment and took a rest from rowing. It was so…peaceful."

A shiver shook her body, whether due to the cold or her memory, I couldn't tell.

"At some point, the captain called for us to continue rowing. Initially, nothing happened, but then, after a few seconds, we heard this high-pitched screech. We looked out the port side and saw this huge thing resembling a giant insect running *on top* of the water towards us. It was huge, the size of ten ships or more. It had eight legs, like a spider, but its legs were very long, stick-like, and they moved so fast. It rushed towards us and had these two giant mandibles that would swing open as it screamed. I later learned previous captains had named the creature Sibyl. It was terrifying."

Sibyl. I had heard this before. But where?

The map. Scribbled beneath Enya on the map were the words "Beware of Sibyl." I had completely forgotten about that warning until now.

Her shivering continued. I wanted to suggest we move inside, but I didn't want to interrupt her story.

"When the creature reached our ship, it immediately tore it to shreds, killing everyone onboard. I got lucky and swam to land before it got me. Our small lifeboat remained intact. As it drifted south under the current, I reached it and eventually found my way back to Anchorville."

"I'm sorry to hear that," Leo said. "I can only imagine what that was like."

Ismay wiped both cheeks with one of her paws. Given the dense snowfall, I hadn't even noticed tears rolling from her eyes as she recalled the memory.

"Ever since then, I've been determined to go back. My brother was on that ship. He was a chemist trying to collect some chai thistle to bring back to his team's lab and study for medicinal purposes. He wanted to find a way to either grow it in the southern region or create new medicine by studying its healing properties. My brother was one of the critters who died. I owe it to him to finish his mission."

Ismay straightened her back, the sadness in her voice giving way to determination. "I've been waiting for a crew headed to Enya with enough capable crewmates to complete the journey. I have to say, I have not seen a crew as passionate and determined as yours. Most crews, by the time they've gone this far, are bickering and complaining, the captain struggling to keep them all rowing in the same direction. You, whatever you've done, is working. It would be an honor to join your crew."

After listening to her story, a yearning to help her finish her brother's mission ignited inside me, fusing with my own yearning to save my daughter. Together, we would reach Enya, I knew it.

"Of course," I said. "We'd be honored to have you join us."

131

Ismay smiled with relief. "Thank you, captain."

"Call me Martin."

Ismay nodded. "Will do." She stepped closer to the door and pulled it open. "Come, let's step inside where it's warm. I have some ideas on how we can get past Sibyl. And I think we ought to let the crew know what they're up against."

# 19

The entire crew decided to stay despite learning about Sibyl, all credit going to Ismay and her plan. Had we learned of Sibyl during the first half of the voyage, my guess is that everyone would've left. More evidence of the benefits of focusing on self-motivated team members rather than those who don't care.

Small chunks of ice drifted in the sea as we moved further north, dancing about the water's surface in celebration of the eternal cold. Still within eyesight of land, we saw massive glaciers carving paths through the mountains as they slowly crawled towards the sea. The sounds of occasional cracking and splashing of ice as it fractured and fell into the water disturbed the otherwise still air.

During her free time, Madeline tinkered in her lab, crafting cloth pouches of her wood-eating acid, wax and varnishes for the ship and oars, and a variety of perfumes and colognes to experiment on the crew. She called the latter "market research" so she could find the best products to sell to shopkeepers.

Francis and Salva quickly became close friends. Upon seeing Salva's wooden net launcher, Francis used his ropemaking skills to design a variety of nets that could be flung off the launcher to land on a school of fish, the weighted ends of the net sinking down and cinching together to trap anything unlucky enough to be caught inside. Through trial and error, they learned how to combine the angle of the launcher with the size and weight of the net to hit their target at various distances. Aside from being cool to watch, this also brought even more fish for Alex to cook and serve.

Thanks to Madeline's waxes, the oars glided in and out of the water like knives through softened butter, allowing the rowers to move faster with less effort. We gained another full day by the time we reached the final port, fully making up for the time we'd lost during the first half of the voyage.

After securing the *Skimmer* at the docks and lowering the gangway, the crew left the ship to explore the tiny town of Anchorville. The town consisted of a single main street with only a couple grub stops, a small Guild Hall, and a sparse collection of shops. Given how few visitors it received, the town didn't even have a sage.

Without needing to recruit anyone, the crew scattered to enjoy some leisure time before the final part of the journey.

Surprisingly, I stumbled into a small artisan shop owned by a large white rabbit named Snowball. Snowball happened to be a weaver by trade, so I allowed myself a couple hours to visit, see his setup, and even have him teach me a few things. The smell of freshly woven yarn and cut cloth wafted through the air in his large shop, reminding me how much I enjoyed weaving and how excited I was to return home.

Snowball let me use his loom, and I quickly wove a small bag to store the chai thistle when we reached Enya. To finish, I sewed a green letter "E" for "Ella" on the brown bag. Weaving this simple bag cleared my mind like a meditation, leaving me relaxed and focused.

I hugged Snowball goodbye, somewhat apprehensive of being crushed by her massive arms, and made my way back towards the ship. Thoughts of the next few days swirled through my mind so quickly that I hardly noticed the grey- and white-furred mouse approaching me. I blinked a few times to make sure I wasn't imagining things.

Artemis.

"Uh, hello Artemis," I said, forcing a smile. Though she wasn't part of my crew and my confidence had grown since we last saw each other, her presence still intimidated me.

"Hello," she said softly. I thought I noticed a hint of tenderness in her voice. My ears must've been malfunctioning. "May I have a word with you?"

What could she want to talk about?

"Sure," I said, unable to think of any reason to decline. She invited me into a small cordial tavern nearby. We sat at the bar and ordered two cherry plum cordials and an apricot scone. A large fire crackled near the bar, basking us in warmth.

"I spoke with Leo," she said as soon as we ordered. "Well, not just Leo, but practically your entire crew."

"Yeah?"

"I have to say, at first, I was convinced there was another captain named Martin sailing the seas. The attitude of your crew couldn't be more different than when I left at Nibbletown. I'm impressed."

A puff of air released from my mouth in a short laugh. "Thank you, that means a lot."

The chipmunk working the bar handed us our cordials and notified us it took a couple minutes to warm the scone.

"What happened?" she said. "When I left, no one wanted to work, everyone was demoralized, and you seemed stressed beyond belief. Now everyone is happy, and you're as relaxed as a bee in honey."

The cool red cordial shot sparks of sweetness and tartness across my tongue. Delicious.

I explained the shifting of my focus from sinkers to rowers and the crew's contributions that led to our successes. I hadn't done anything special. Really, more than anything, I just empowered the crew and then got out of their way. It seemed almost like cheating.

"I see," she said, taking a sip of her cordial.

The chipmunk set a triangular scone on the bar between us, thin layers of smoke rising and fading into the air.

"Well, I'm impressed. You've changed quite a bit in such a short period of time." She ripped off a piece of scone and slipped it into her mouth.

"Thank you. What are you doing here? Is your new crew here?"

"No," she said in between chews of the pastry. She swallowed before continuing. "Max, you remember him, the bulky mouse who used to be on your crew?"

I nodded.

"We both joined another crew on a large ship that moved much faster than yours. However, a few days ago, the crew was on the verge of mutiny, so we left."

"Really? What happened?"

136

"The captain we sailed under was too closed-minded, never willing to change her opinion on anything nor listen to the crew. So after we left, we decided to wait here for a week or so to join another crew. Or, if we didn't find one, sail back south."

"I'm sorry to hear that," I said, grabbing a piece of the scone for myself. Then, after a moment of silence, I asked, "Have you always worked at sea?"

She looked at me, slightly surprised at my question. "Why do you ask?"

"Well," I said, "to be perfectly honest, you're very intimidating." She laughed, inviting me to smile as well. "You seem so confident with such little tolerance for a crew who doesn't know what they're doing. I assumed you've been doing this your whole life, but figured I'd ask."

I popped the piece of scone in my mouth. Its warmth pleasantly contrasted with the coolness of the cordial. Again, delicious.

"I've been on the seas for a while. A little too long, to be honest. Though my passion is performing. When my sister Heather and I were younger, we joined a traveling acrobat group. We traveled all over and performed with them. Aerial acrobats. That was our specialty. The two of us would swing from ropes as high as the tallest trees. We'd swing back and forth, flip through the air, catch each other, and do a variety of other stunts. We loved it."

"Why don't you still do that?"

Artemis breathed deeply. "During one of our performances, I messed up. I forgot to chalk my paws between acts. When I caught her, my paw was too slippery to hold on, and…I dropped her."

137

A gasp was all I could manage in my surprise. Had her sister died?

"Fortunately, tree branches broke her fall the best they could. They spared her life but broke her ribs and arm, so she could no longer perform." I remained quiet as she took a sip of her cordial. "I refuse to act without her, especially since her injury is due to my carelessness."

"Do you think she'll be able to perform again?"

"I'm not sure. I'm trying to save up enough money to take her to a surgeon who specializes in her types of injuries, which is why I choose the most dangerous voyages like yours that typically pay the best. I suppose it's also why I have such a low tolerance for incompetence, no offense."

"None taken," I said, and I meant it. Though her situation differed from mine, I understood her passion for completing her mission and her resentment for anything standing in her way. "I'm sorry to hear about Heather. I hope she's able to get the surgery she needs and you two get the chance to perform again soon."

"Thank you, Martin. Me too." She slipped another piece of scone in her mouth and then pushed the plate towards me, indicating the rest was mine. "So, I know you don't have any crew positions open, but I was wondering if Max and I could rejoin."

My eyes widened. This was unexpected. "I don't have any open positions."

She smiled. "I know. I just said that."

"I...can't afford to pay you anything," I said, ashamed of my lack of resources.

"No payment needed. If you don't take us, more than likely we'll have to pay for a ferry back to Cherrystone. Max has secured quite a variety of metals for his blacksmithing shop back home, so a ferry allowing that much cargo would be costly. Joining you would save us money, not to mention the free food we'd get. Word on the trail is Alex's food is quite exquisite these days." She grinned playfully.

It would be nice to have both of them aboard. "Are you sure?" I asked.

"Positive."

"Then of course I could use the help. Did the crew tell you about Sibyl?"

"They did."

"And you still want to join?"

"How many times are you going to ask me that?" Irritation crept back into her tone.

"Okay, okay," I said, not wanting to sour her mood. "I'd love to have you two back. I'm sure you'll be a huge help."

"Great," she said smiling. She kicked back her stool, stood up, and faced the bartender. "He's ready for the check." Her eyes darted back to me with a slightly devious grin. "See you on the *Skimmer*, captain."

# 20

Max and Artemis fit right in. Having two extra crew members increased our speed by shortening the shifts and allowing more rest. Both had several ideas they shared with me, and, aligning with my new management style, I simply empowered them, offered my support, and stayed out of their way.

Land vanished from view shortly after leaving Anchorville, leaving us alone in the cold, open water. Ismay helped with any navigation issues as she'd traveled this distance twice. Other than a few minor hiccups here or there, nothing disturbed us until at last, land up ahead came into view.

Enya.

Massive mountains stabbed up from the ground and pierced the sky, lancing towards the heavens. Even from a distance, the mountains looked impenetrable, too steep to climb and too wild to conquer. Yet patches of greenery managed to cling to their sides, a testament to the resilience of life in the face of adversity.

As we drew closer, I noticed a narrow gap that sliced through the land giants, serving as the only entrance into the mountainous kingdom. It looked like a jagged wound in the earth, a gateway to some hidden world beyond. We had come so far, endured so much, and now, we had finally arrived at our destination.

I had spent so many nights dreaming of the day we'd finally arrive at Enya, imagining the island as some tropical paradise, a gift from the heavens to reward us for completing such a long and strenuous journey.

Instead, Enya stood before us like a forbidding fortress, surrounded by icy waters that seemed to warn sailors of the dangers within. A sense of numbness swept through my body as we glided towards the imposing island that either held the cure for my daughter or the end of our journey.

Lost in my thoughts, I barely registered the movements of Ismay and Leo as they guided our vessel towards the narrow gap. The crew stood in silent awe as we slipped into the opening and entered the island of Enya.

We moved much slower in this narrow passageway, not wanting to accidentally hit any rocks. The entire crew gathered above deck on either side of the *Skimmer* to gaze at the steep, unsettling cliffs that shot straight up alongside us, forming a narrow corridor that whispered of threats and danger. If a single rock or boulder fell from any of the cliffs and hit the *Skimmer*, we'd most certainly sink.

Fortunately, the passageway remained relatively straight, allowing us to glide through the still water between the cliffs. After several hours, we noticed up ahead the passage opened into a huge lake.

"Let's slow her down," Ismay said as soon as the lake came into view. "Let's stop the *Skimmer* just shy of the lake."

Then she turned to look at Leo and me. "That's where Sibyl lives."

# 21

All dozen oars dipped down, the wide ends pushing against the calm water and sending ripples rolling outwards until the *Skimmer* came to a stop about a hundred yards from the lake's entrance.

Per Ismay's suggestion, we let the entire crew take a break, encouraging them to eat a light snack and rest. Ismay, Leo, Artemis, and I gathered at the front of the ship to go over the plan.

Around the lake, the pink and purple petals decorating the trees remained perfectly still in the absence of wind. The lake looked so pretty, so inviting. How could such a foul creature live here?

"Look out, straight ahead," Ismay said, handing me the spyglass.

Peering through the spyglass, the lake magnified as it jumped closer. I could see the other side clearly, and I saw the lake's exit, a narrow passageway like the one protecting us now. I handed the spyglass to Leo, then looked at Ismay.

"Fortunately," Ismay said. "The exit is straight ahead." She pointed to the exit, out of view without the aid of the spyglass. "As I said before, I believe Sibyl is blind, or it would've seen me drifting away from the wreckage. I think it detects prey through movement and sound. Everything remained calm on my last voyage when we just drifted into the lake. It was only when we started rowing that the beast attacked."

Leo handed the spyglass to Artemis, who glanced through it briefly and handed it back to Ismay.

"Given the presence of driftwood in the lake, I don't think the beast identifies floating objects as prey. It seems to only attack disturbances in the water. The current is light, so if we get enough speed and aim ourselves perfectly straight, we should be able to drift across the lake undetected and slip into the passageway on the other side."

"How do you know we'll be safe if we reach the passage?" I asked. "Won't Sibyl detect us when we finally do start rowing again?"

"Sibyl is too large to fit through the passage. Besides, rocks fall from the cliffs all the time, so I'm assuming it doesn't pay much attention to movement in that area. Obviously, I've never been on the other side, so I could be wrong. But this is the only way to reach inland. This entire island is surrounded by cliffs too steep to climb. We either cross this lake, or we go home."

I approached the rails, allowing my paws to slowly grip the smooth wood. Stillness imprisoned the water and trees, keeping everything eerily quiet.

This was it. Everything we'd been through the past five weeks had all been leading up to this moment. All the meetings, one-on-ones, visits with the sages, arguments, pep talks, everything…it had all led to this.

I thanked the forest for my crew. Leo, Ismay, Artemis, Max, Alex, Salva, Madeline, and all the others. Without their ideas and suggestions, their genuine desire to help and do good…without them, this would have been impossible. We probably wouldn't even have made it this far.

This could be the end for me, or this could be a new beginning. Either way, all the pieces were locked together for success. All the preparations were complete; now it was time to act.

"Let's do this," I said.

We turned back to the ship and prepared the crew. Salva, Madeline, and Francis worked together to set up the net launcher and its two different types of ammunition: acid pouches courtesy of Madeline and giant nets courtesy of Francis. Harry passed around shots of one of his energy cocktails to kickstart everyone's adrenaline. Max, the bulkiest critter on board, took the front rowing position, hoping his energy and speed would spread throughout the crew.

As everyone settled in, I took my spot on the other front oar, port side, opposite of Max.

Given Ismay's experience, I gave her command of the crew to get us into the lake. With all the crew in position, she had them all row in reverse, giving us as much room as possible to build up speed.

"Remember," she called out to everyone. "It's not only important that we go fast; we must also go straight. If one side rows even slightly faster than the other, the *Skimmer* will favor the opposite side. Given the length of the lake, even a few degrees will send us off course. Unfortunately, we can't risk calling out when to row to avoid alerting Sibyl, so you'll have to be mindful of your crewmates. Max and the captain will row in sync with each other. Everyone else, just focus on the critter directly in front of you and mimic their speed and form."

Coming to a bend in the passage behind us, the *Skimmer* came to a stop.

"We got this," Artemis said, manning the oar behind me. I nodded, my heart pumping too strongly for me to form a verbal response.

"Everyone ready?" Ismay called out, standing at the front of the ship, holding the spyglass by her side.

The crew nodded, some gave a chant of readiness, others simply straightened their backs in preparation.

"Okay," Ismay said, turning forward to face the lake. Leo stepped to her side, ready to direct us should one side fall out of sync with the other.

Ismay held up her paw, straight to the sky.

Then her arm fell forward, pointing down the passage.

"Row!"

# 22

Up, forward, down, back.

Up, forward, down, back.

During the storm, I rowed as fast as possible. That singular goal made it easy to tap into all my energy and put it to use. This, however, presented a different challenge. We needed to both go as fast as possible while also staying in sync. A tug-of-war ensued in my mind between moving faster and slowing down to make sure my speed didn't surpass Max's.

At first, Max and I focused too intently on staying in sync at the expense of speed. Leo's paw circled the air in front of himself several times in a beckoning motion, indicating we needed to pick up the pace. We were being too cautious.

Up, forward, down, back.

I moved quicker, more confidently, plunging my oar deep into the glass-like water, gaining as much propulsion per stroke as possible. Max picked up his pacing as well; the wind's blow over our whiskers indicated a gain in speed.

Leo gave an approving nod, yet kept motioning with his paw for us to go faster. We were in sync. Time to shed even more caution and row.

The *Skimmer* swam forward with quickening speed. The faster she moved, the easier it became to row. Seeing the lake's mouth approaching intensified my resolve, and I began to lose myself in the rhythm. Every stroke was one stroke closer to our last. We needed enough momentum to completely cross the lake to have any chance.

Up, forward, down, back.

About fifty yards until we reached the lake. The air rushed past us faster as we gained speed.

Forty. Thirty. Twenty.

We moved so fast the last few yards whizzed by in the flick of a tail. Leo motioned upward with his paw, and we all stabilized the oars out of the water as the *Skimmer* slipped into the lake.

Unsure if the creature could hear our footsteps, we slowly rose to our feet, crept across the deck to the rails on either side, and scanned the lake for signs of danger.

The lake felt like an entirely different world. Coldness surrendered to warmth, and pink- and purple-leafed trees brightened the air. The lake's surface resembled a giant ovular mirror, reflecting everything back up into the sky with perfect clarity. Staring at my reflection, the water seemed to reflect not only my physical presence, but also my thoughts. My beady eyes shrunk under cover of my whiskers and fur, staring down into the water and back up into themselves. I looked so tiny against the backdrop of the sky. So small, so fragile, so weak....

My eyes snapped shut. I shook my head to clear my thoughts, and then gazed out over the lake. This serene oasis in the mountains offered no signs of threat. If this Sibyl was as big as Ismay described, surely it would be visible now, wouldn't it? Maybe Sibyl had found a way to escape into the ocean.

We drifted about a fourth of the way across the lake and still moved at a decent pace. Speed seemed about right. Hopefully, we had the right heading as well.

I stepped away from the rail and cautiously walked across the deck towards Ismay, still up at the front peering through her spyglass. I made eye contact with several of the crew. Despite the heavy silence, I sensed how they felt and heard their thoughts.

Reaching Ismay, I put my paw on her shoulder to avoid startling her. She turned to face me, and my eyes asked: *How's our heading?*

She breathed slowly, looked slightly downward, and shook her head. Feeling the spyglass slip into my paw, I gripped it, raised it up, and looked through. Too far on the starboard side. We weren't even halfway across the lake, and our destination presented itself clearly: if we didn't change direction, we would run aground to the right of the exit.

We weren't going to make it.

I lowered the eyeglass. Too far to the right meant that the port side, *my* side, rowed quicker than the starboard. My cheeks warmed as I scolded myself. I went too fast.

Leo gently tugged the spyglass through my weakening grip to check for himself.

I scanned the lake again for danger. Nothing.

We passed halfway.

We were getting close. We needed to change our heading. The longer we waited, the more dramatic our change would need to be. If we tried changing course now, we'd make less noise; however, if Sibyl heard us, we'd have longer to outrun it. If we waited, we'd be at greater risk of Sibyl detecting us but would have a shorter distance to safety.

Mentally, I flipped through these two options. Each heavy second that passed slowly made the decision for me. Inaction was an action.

I looked up at Leo. I needed to speak. Silence cost too much.

"I think we should fix our heading now," I whispered. "Before it's too late."

Artemis, Leo, and Ismay huddled around, all looking at each other first, and then Ismay nodded in agreement.

Silently, we ushered the crew to assume their positions on the oars, although I had a crewmate take mine so I could remain with Leo and Ismay up front. We didn't have to inform anyone our heading was off—they all knew it. The crew exchanged unsettled glances at one another as they got into position, gripped their oars, and looked up at us, waiting for our orders.

Facing the crew, I held up my right hand, signaling for the port side to ready their oars. Their grips tightened around the oars, hovering them inches above the reflective water.

Pointing my palm downward, I very, very slowly lowered my paw.

Following my instruction, the crew slowly lowered their oars until the tips barely broke the water's surface. My paw continued to lower, and they followed suit, fully submerging the oars into the lake. The water delicately collided with the oars, pushing against them with unyielding strength, slowly turning the *Skimmer* to the port side.

I allowed my breath to release as I felt the boat turn. Glancing behind me, Leo motioned to hold steady until Ismay gave the all-clear.

An ear-splitting screech shattered the peaceful silence around the lake. Water erupted in the distance as a massive creature jumped up, spinning in the air and shedding the water latched to its body. Eight bony legs snapped outward, and then it spun like a massive helicopter seed as it descended back down to the lake. When its legs touched the water, rather than breaking through, they pushed down, creating small wells around each of its legs, the water's surface tension remaining unbroken. It defied gravity this way…much like monsters in storybooks.

It wasn't until the creature spun around that I realized it hadn't been facing us.

Two yellow eyes narrowed directly at us. My skin prickled.

Its mandibles swung open, revealing a mouth crowded with razor-sharp teeth. I covered my ears as it released another deafening scream and then watched in horror as it charged towards us.

# 23

My conscious mind thrust controls to my subconscious again. Instinct took over.

"Oars up, both sides!" I shouted. When they complied and were ready to all row in sync, I continued. "Row! Full speed ahead!" I turned and pointed for the exit. "There's your target. Ignore everything going on around you, just focus on getting the *Skimmer* to that passage. Our lives depend on you."

I turned to Ismay. "Guide us to that passage." She nodded. Then to Leo and Artemis: "With me."

I rushed to the rear starboard side, the closest part of the ship to Sibyl. The creature's ridiculous size negated the need for a spyglass. It rushed towards us over the water with the grace of a water strider and ferocity of a spider. Whatever it was, it would tear this ship apart within seconds of reaching it. We needed to outrun it.

I watched the creature race across the water for a few seconds, mentally calculating its velocity. Turning to the exit, I calculated our speed to see if we would make it. We wouldn't.

"We're not going to make it," I said.

"We're going to have to fight it," Artemis said, stepping up to the rail.

I spun around and shouted. "Salva! Madeline!"

The two rushed over upon hearing their names.

"We aren't going to make it to the exit," I said when they stopped in front of me. "We need to slow it down. Salva, prepare your net launcher off the starboard aft. Madeline, ready your acid pouches. Let's hope your acid eats through whatever that thing is."

"Aye, Cap'n," they both said in unison and scurried off.

I turned back to face Sibyl, still charging closer with hatred in its supposedly blind eyes. The *Skimmer* picked up speed, though not enough to outpace the monster.

Max rushed up to the quarterdeck beside us, heaving a barrel over his massive shoulder.

"Captain," he said. "That creature can only sense disturbances in the water. What if I toss this here barrel off the starboard side when it gets close? It could distract it, buy us some time."

"Good idea," I said. Gauging by Sibyl's speed, it would reach us in less than a minute. "Get ready and wait for my command."

Max nodded and positioned himself near the rail.

A gust of wind brushed my face as Salva whizzed past, setting up his net launcher angled up against the rail. His net launcher resembled a mini cannon. He pushed some gunpowder into the tube, and then Madeline slipped in one of her acid pouches. We heard the soft *thump* as the pouch slid down and bumped against the powder. Artemis lifted the small carton of matches and carried it next to Madeline. Madeline quickly removed a match from the container while Artemis held it, and then using both paws, she readied it against the striking strip. Salva positioned himself at the base of the launcher, closing one eye and using the other to aim.

Thirty seconds from impact with Sibyl.

As the creature drew closer, its massive size became even more apparent. An entire ship could fit in just its central body alone, not counting its large, bony legs and giant mandibles. Its body remained still as its legs moved in perfect harmony to carry it effortlessly over the water. Its mandibles quivered, allowing short hisses to escape its foul mouth as it moved. It was a ballet of death and destruction, and it danced toward us at frightening speed.

"By the redwoods," Leo said. "I've never seen anything like this."

"Max, now!" I yelled.

Max spun around and heaved the barrel up over the rail, several yards away from the ship. It landed with the thud of a cannonball into the lake, blasting water up all around it.

Sibyl's head snapped to the side in the direction of the barrel. It rocketed forward, spread its mandibles wide, and chomped down on the barrel, obliterating it instantly. Tiny chunks of wood sprayed from its mouth as it devoured the barrel and all its contents, creating a firework show of timber. Without skipping a beat, Sibyl turned back towards us and charged even faster, as if it understood we'd tricked it and was angered by our ruse.

The distraction bought us ten seconds, no more.

"Ready…" I said to Madeline and Salva, raising my hand.

Salva adjusted the launcher to point at Sibyl, making tiny

adjustments to account for Sibyl's changing position.

Madeline tightened her grip on the match.

Sibyl's shadow overtook the ship as it towered over us, ready to strike.

"Fire!" I shouted.

Madeline twisted her body, striking the match against the strip and then igniting the wick. The flame rocketed down the wick to feast on the gunpowder.

Sibyl's mandibles widened, presenting us with several rows of razor-sharp teeth. The tip of its mandibles began wrapping around the *Skimmer*. Any second, they would snap shut and rip right through us.

*Boom!*

The explosion sent the acid pouch hurtling out of the launcher, up in the air, arching up, up, up until it crashed into Sibyl's face.

Sibyl's legs smashed down into the water as it cried out in rage. No longer properly supporting itself, Sibyl began to sink.

"Duck!" Max shouted.

Sibyl's head twisted as its body fell into the water, causing one of its mandibles to swing towards us. The rail opposite us snapped and splintered as the mandible crashed into it and began sweeping over the deck.

Everyone around me dropped to their bellies, flattening themselves as much as possible.

Everyone except Leo.

Leo moved to lie down, but with his peg leg, he wasn't fast enough.

Without thinking, I leapt towards him. As soon as my paws grabbed him, I shoved him forward with all my might, pushing him as far away as I could. My body in mid-air, Sibyl's mandible crashed into my left leg—

My bone snapped—

My broken leg searing with pain, my body flailed in the air, off the ship, and then into the lake.

# 24

Memories of Ella flooded my mind.

I saw us foraging berries together.

Then I saw her hiding behind a tree in a game of hide-and-seek.

Then she was helping her mother bake some blueberry muffins.

Next, she came rushing towards me, arms wide, and leapt into the air to hug me, beyond excited to see me after a recent trip. Her soft fur nestled against the side of my face, her tiny arms squeezing me as tightly as she could, as if any distance between us presented a problem.

Water splashed in the background, sounding far off in the distance, barely audible.

Cold flooded into my body as a new memory faded into view: that of Ella in the hospital, lying on the bed unconscious, Doctor Farah standing by her side, pressing her paw against my daughter's forehead.

Realization I had failed hit me like a brick. Darkness clouded my peripheral vision, reducing my vision to a circle that slowly started shrinking.

I heard a massive monster in the background, crying out in pain and fury, thrashing about in the water.

The circle continued to shrink around the memory. I fought to slow the darkness, but it continued. As the memory shrank, Doctor Farah slowly faded from view, leaving just Ella on the bed.

And then just Ella.

And then only her face. My daughter, alone, her life slipping away, just like mine.

Then she, too, faded.

My vision went black.

I drifted in nothingness.

Was I alive? Was I dead? I didn't know. Nor did I care. Even if I was alive, I certainly wouldn't last long, bobbing in the water with a broken leg next to a monstrous sea creature.

Either way, it would be over soon.

I'm sorry, Ella.

...

A splash. This one I heard clearly. Water sprayed over my face.

Voices, in the distance. Faint, as if searching for me, and then growing louder, clearer.

"Captain!" one of the voices said.

"Grab on!"

"Quick!"

I opened one eye, and then the other.

A rope rested atop the water next to me. The rope was moving, being pulled away. I saw the end a few feet away. Within seconds, it would slip out of reach.

Mustering all my energy, I lifted my arm, moved my paw under the rope, grabbed on, and squeezed tightly as the rope began pulling my body across the water.

Slowly, my senses came back to me. The horrible thrashing and wailing of Sibyl returned, and I looked over my legs being dragged through the water to see the creature still struggling to regain its footing.

I looked back over my shoulder, my gaze riding the rope all the way up to where it was fastened on the *Skimmer*. Francis, Salva, Madeline, and many others stood at the aft, cheering and encouraging me to hold on. I saw another crew member watching: Leo. He made it.

The rope lurched forward, pulling me in closer for a second and then pausing. Then another tug. Looking closer, I saw Max holding onto the rope, pulling me closer, one massive tug at a time.

"Come on, captain!" Ismay shouted through cupped paws around her mouth. "Pull your way up!"

A loud screech erupted in the distance. I looked back over my limp body and saw Sibyl stabilize itself over the water. Green acid dripped from its face as it glared at me with newfound fury.

"Hurry!" Madeline shouted from the ship.

The creature yelled again and started rushing towards me.

Strength rushed back into me. It wasn't over yet. I still had a chance. I needed to move.

Turning over onto my stomach, I grabbed the rope with my other hand. Squeezing tightly, I moved one paw above the other, grabbed the rope, and pulled myself closer to the ship.

"Ah!" I cried in pain as my broken leg sent a sharp pulse through my body. Clenching my teeth, I moved my left paw above my right, gripped, and pulled.

Then another tug from Max pulled me closer.

161

It was working.

After stabilizing itself, Sibyl raced towards me. The water shook as it got closer. I glanced over my shoulder. The creature towered over me. There was no more time. Sibyl screamed and prepared to lunge.

*Boom!*

A net launched across the sky and landed directly on the joint of one of Sibyl's legs, causing its leg to collapse inward, forcing it off-balance and giving me more time.

I turned back to the ship and pulled myself forward.

Behind me, I heard the creature ripping the net constricting its leg and continuing its pursuit.

*Boom!*

An acid pouch sailed overhead, detonating over the creature, causing it to hiss and wail.

It continued its pursuit; I continued climbing; Max continued pulling.

Madeline and Salva pelted the creature with nets and acid, doing everything they could to buy Max and me enough time to get me aboard.

I grabbed with my right paw, pulled, then my left. I climbed with everything I had. My chest and arms burned; my leg felt as if a knife kept stabbing into it and twisting. But I had hope. Without crewmates like Madeline and Salva, Leo and Ismay, Artemis and Max, I'd be dead right now, and my daughter with me. If we somehow managed to get through this, it would only be due to having a team of rowers.

Right. Left. *Boom!* Right. Left.

Nearly there. Just a few more pulls.

Right. Left.

"Come on captain!" Leo yelled.

I kept climbing. Max kept pulling. Finally, my body rose from the water as I was pulled up towards the deck.

A few more pulls until I reached him.

Suddenly, one of Sibyl's legs flicked sideways against the rope between Max and me. The sudden force flung me up slightly, and then another of Sibyl's legs slammed against my side from underneath, catapulting me up high in the air—

My limbs flailed about, trying to find something to grab, but there was nothing. Just air.

I looked down below and saw Sibyl's head moving under me, its mandibles opened wide. Gravity yanked me downward towards its mouth, its hot breath choking my lungs.

I fell. Unable to grab anything, my body surrendered to gravity's pull and dropped downward into its mouth.

A flash of gray and white from the side.

Artemis.

I looked over to see the fierce mouse swinging towards me, one paw holding onto a rope tied to one of the masts, the other stretched out to grab me. She swung with acrobatic precision directly towards me—

Her arm collided against my side, knocking the wind out of me. She pulled me close, hugging me with all her might as we swung together away from Sibyl's mouth and towards the ship.

The creature's jaws slammed shut behind us as we swung around towards the *Skimmer*. Once safely over the deck, she released me, and we both fell and tumbled as we landed.

*Boom!* Madeline and Salva launched another acid pouch, directly over Sibyl's mouth—Sibyl's scream shook the air.

"Another!" Artemis yelled at Madeline and Salva, quickly springing to her feet.

*Boom!*

"Keep rowing!" Ismay shouted from the front.

I looked up to the sky and saw towering cliffs roll into view.

The passage.

The crew sent an unrelenting barrage of acid and nets at Sibyl, keeping it at bay until we slipped into the narrow passage and exited the lake.

I collapsed onto my back, arms and legs spread over the deck, panting heavily.

We made it.

# 25

I hobbled on my new crutches across flat ground, keeping my bandaged leg straight and safe from any pressure. Illuminated by the late-evening sun, purple and pink blooms flowed over the ground, shivering slightly under the gentle breeze. The soft soil felt delightful under my good paw as I walked. There were no trails or paths here: nature in its truest form.

Harry's medicinal herbs and salves saved my leg. Had he not joined the crew, infection would've destroyed my bone and muscle, causing me to likely lose the limb. Or my life.

The crew walked ahead, some taking in the beautiful view, others talking excitedly. They all wanted to race ahead to the pond where we would hopefully find chai thistle, but they slowed their pace on my behalf.

I continued hobbling forward as fast as I could through the flowers over the soft soil. Too mentally and physically exhausted for conversation, I took this time to reflect on what I'd learned.

The conversation with Luna saved this voyage. Had I continued my then-current strategy, spending all my time with those critters causing the most problems, I would've continued neglecting those providing the most value. I would have spent all my energy trying to motivate those who aren't naturally motivated, like pouring water into a cup with a tiny hole in the bottom. I'd fill it up, it would slowly drain, and then I'd need to fill it up again. There are only so many cups I could fill in a day.

Managing that way drained me. Not only was it a waste of my time, but I was hurting the rowers—actively demotivating them. If a rower worked twice as hard as everyone else and got the least amount of my time and support, how would that make her feel? Or if a rower worked even harder to make up for all the sinkers, how would *that* make her feel? That wouldn't be a very enjoyable environment, so she would eventually either get pulled down and become a sinker or leave to find a team where she wouldn't have to make up for everyone else's slack.

As rowers left or dropped down to sinkers, it became harder to recruit new rowers. No rower wanted to work with a team of sinkers. Even without a magic monocle, a rower could simply glance at the overall team culture to get a feel for whether it was fueled by rowers or sinkers.

Over time, the rowers left or became disenchanted, sinkers attracted other sinkers, and the team got polluted with negativity. No one was happy, and the work didn't get done.

This was a mistake most leaders made, including my father, including myself.

*Motivating others is a waste of time. Instead, find self-motivated critters, and work your tail off to make sure you don't demotivate them.*

That summary of Luna's advice changed everything for me.

Rowers were self-motivated. They didn't need to be micromanaged, they didn't need daily pep-talks, they didn't need to be told every detail of how to do their job. They simply needed to be given a goal, informed of any boundaries to stay within, empowered, and then left alone to thrive.

Time spent with rowers was bliss and nearly always led to new ideas and opportunities as we synergized together. When I tried to tackle problems on by myself, making unilateral decisions and then directing their team to follow, it didn't work well. Instead, inviting rowers to collaborate solved problems better and faster. And because they were part of the solutions, the rowers took ownership in executing them, making sure the solutions worked and course-correcting when they didn't.

Whenever a sinker slipped into the team, the time to act was *now*. Putting it off only created bigger problems. Every day the sinker stayed on further demotivated the rowers. Keeping sinkers aboard was bad for everyone involved. If left unchecked, the entire team would implode.

A sinker could be a sinker due to a lack of training, support, tools, misunderstanding of the goal, or something else that was my responsibility to provide. Other times, there could be a cultural mismatch, in which case I needed to identify the misalignment and decide whether the current culture should be changed.

But when I had exhausted all options and the sinker was still a sinker, the sinker needed to separate from the crew. Every day I put off dealing with the problem was a day from the sinker's life. I put off firing critters because I thought I was doing them a favor, but I was only doing myself the favor of avoiding a difficult conversation at their expense. Life is short. I owed it to the sinkers to give them as much of their life back as possible to find a team with which they resonate.

By following those guidelines, I was able to turn the crew around.

Had I not refocused on taking care of my rowers, Leo and Alex wouldn't have stayed on. They created an atmosphere that enabled rowers to flourish. This created a crew that attracted even more rowers, which led to critters like Harry joining, whose medicine saved my leg; Salva, Madeline, and Francis, whose net launcher, acid, and rope nets saved our entire crew; Max, whose strength pulled me away from Sibyl's grasp; Ismay, whose knowledge of Enya proved invaluable; and Artemis, whose acrobatic skills saved me from Sibyl. And so on.

A manager's job isn't to figure out how to solve all the problems. I didn't think of the net launcher, the acid, the rope, understanding how Sibyl detects its prey…any of that.

*A manager's primary job is to build a team of rowers.* That's it.

I thought my job was to figure out what should happen and then find critters to do it. I learned it's easier and usually more effective to instead focus on getting the right critters on the team and *together* figuring out what to do or where to go.

"We're there," Leo whispered into my ear, pulling me from my thoughts.

I looked up and saw the crew gathered around a small pond ahead. Increasing my pace, I hobbled closer to the water.

Thin green stalks with pointy leaves poked up from the ground all along the water's edge, encircling the entire pond. The tops of each flower held small spherical bobs colored a deep purple. Tiny whisker-like purple petals resembling blades of grass surrounded those small spheres in a protective embrace.

When I reached one, with some effort and Alex's help, I sat on the grass and reached over to rub my finger over the flower.

*Chai thistle.*

We found it.

# 26

"Martin!" Doctor Farah said as I entered her office two weeks later. Thanks to the sails and crew, the voyage back offered no challenges or surprises (it was far easier crossing Sibyl's lake with sails instead of oars).

I dropped the bag I had woven in Anchorville on her desk.

She leaned forward, pulling open the pouch just enough to see inside. Her eyes widened and then her gaze shifted back up to me. "Chai thistle?"

I nodded.

"This is perfect!" she stood up, grabbing the pouch. "I'll start Ella's treatment right away."

I remained by Ella's side for the next twenty-four hours. Maybe longer. Time no longer registered with me. My mission complete, my only responsibility was remaining by my daughter's side until she recovered.

Sitting in one of the wooden chairs, I drifted off into my thoughts. I couldn't help but laugh at how it all started with Rico simply trying to sell me his monocle. At the time, I wanted nothing to do with him and hoped he would simply leave me alone. But without the monocle, I never would've made it.

When we returned from Enya, Rico, ever the merchant, hired a crew of critters to sail back to Enya and procure more chai thistle. Rico paid for the installation of a large rudder on the back of his ship to allow them to control the ship's direction without needing to use oars. This allowed them to sail past Sibyl more easily and reliably.

With much of the danger removed, he could repeatedly send voyages to Enya, procure chai thistle, and then rush to deliver it to the various healing centers to help save more critters like Ella. He also promised to deliver a steady supply of chai thistle to Ismay so she could continue her brother's work of finding some way to domesticate the herb so they could grow it locally. Although Raccoon Rita didn't give the best advice on managing others, she was right to advise me to keep Rico close.

Thoughts continued floating in my head as I dozed off. Unable to sleep through the night, I instead sprinkled my day with catnaps (such a frightening name for a short nap). After a while, in that weird state of being in a dream while also recognizing that I *was* in a dream, I watched myself working on a tunic calmly and peacefully in my shop, removed from all the chaos of managing a crew. Suddenly, the door to my shop swung open, and, of course, Rico popped in saying his usual: "Imagine working in your shop with *thiiis!*"

He reached inside his coat of seemingly infinite gadgets to pull something out—and then I heard a voice.

"Dad?"

# A Note from the Author

I hope you enjoyed *Journey to Enya*!

Martin's story follows a similar arc to my own. I opened my first business 14 years ago. Like him, I spent most of my time focusing on the team members who caused the most problems. I was miserable, they were miserable, and my businesses struggled.

As soon as I adopted the mindset of focusing on the superstars instead, everything changed for the better.

Here are some thoughts on managing others. I'm not suggesting this is the absolute best way to handle every possible team interaction; I'm simply presenting my personal experience and management style. These are general rules of thumb that I've followed that have led to positive results.

## *Rowers, Watchers & Sinkers Defined*

Below are some broad descriptions of Rowers, Watchers, and Sinkers.

**Rowers:** Team members who are passionate about their work. They come to work with a positive attitude, align with the culture's core values, enjoy achieving goals and success, take initiative, come up with new ideas for growth, and genuinely care about the company. Most importantly, *they are self-motivated.*

**Watchers:** Watchers come in, do their job, and go home. They don't typically generate new ideas nor look for ways to exceed expectations. They follow all the policies and procedures and do a relatively good job. While they may enjoy their job, they primarily view work as a way to collect a paycheck vs an opportunity to excel and grow.

**Sinkers:** Sinkers actively try to sink the ship. They complain, create a toxic environment, organize mutinies, love finding problems and spreading gossip, blame everyone but themselves for problems, hate taking accountability, and do the bare minimum (or less) that's required of them.

Real life isn't as simple as this, so certain team members may be a blend of two or even three of these categories. We could create many more categories and sub-categories. But simplifying the categories down to three vs dozens makes it easier to strategize how to manage a team, even if we lose a little bit of accuracy with each label—much like using a map to navigate a trail even though it doesn't specify the exact location of every tree.

## A Manager's Primary Job

A manager's primary job is building a team of Rowers.

A manager's primary job is *not* working hard, putting in a lot of hours, checking boxes, completing tasks, staying busy, nor anything else. A manager should be obsessed with finding, cultivating, and empowering Rowers.

## *Rowers*

Rowers are awesome. Rowers are gold. Taking a Rower for granted is a horrible and costly mistake.

A leader's number one job with Rowers is to *make sure they don't become demotivated.*

Rowers are self-motivated. They don't need constant pep talks. They aren't taking up a bunch of the manager's time complaining. They don't need to be micromanaged.

But they can be demotivated if they don't feel the leader is supporting them or holding others accountable.

I spend as much time as I can with Rowers, but not managing them or making sure they're doing their job. Instead, I ask for their ideas, their opinions on challenges I'm facing, if there's anything I can do to better support them, and if there's any extra responsibilities they'd like to take on. I also get to know their personal and professional goals and strive to help them achieve them. I invest in them as people, not as employees simply moving the company forward.

Whenever I have an idea for the company, I run it past them to get their opinions. I love when Rowers disagree with me, and I encourage them to challenge and expand my perspective.

177

I give my Rowers power and authority. I've found the most success by pushing authority down as much as possible vs keeping it for myself. Telling a Rower to take initiative but run everything past me for approval provides too much friction for them. I want them to embrace their creativity and try things, even if they make a mistake.

In fact, I encourage them to make mistakes. I set a goal for my leaders to make at least four mistakes every year. If they make fewer than four mistakes, it means they aren't taking enough risks or trying enough new things. By default, most people are hyper-focused on being perfect, not making mistakes, and avoiding getting into trouble. People aren't perfect and they *should* make mistakes as long as their intentions are genuine.

When I finally get a Rower on my team, they get all my love and attention. If I ever get the slightest hint they're becoming demotivated, I immediately address it.

## Watchers

While getting a team consisting 100% of Rowers is ideal, life isn't ideal. I've never managed to have a team of only Rowers.

Watchers are fine. They get the job done, they're reliable, and they don't slow anyone down. When they have concerns, I address them, but I don't go out of my way to run all my ideas past them.

## *Sinkers*

The word "sinkers" has a negative connotation, but it doesn't mean that people labeled as sinkers are bad people. In fact, once a team member is first identified as a Sinker, I first look inward to see if there's anything I or the business is doing or not doing that is causing him to be a Sinker.

The most common culprits that lead to team members becoming Sinkers are:

- They don't know what to do.
  - No one told them to vacuum the store, so they didn't.
- They don't know how to do it.
  - No one trained them how to use the vacuum, what to do if it's clogged, where to find spare bags, etc.
- They don't have clear expectations.
  - Should they simply run the vacuum down the center of each aisle and prioritize efficiency? Or should they go up and down every aisle multiple times to cover its entire width and prioritize thoroughness?
  - Should they also vacuum behind the counter?
  - How long should vacuuming take? Is it better to take thirty minutes and vacuum 80% of the store, or two hours and vacuum 100% of the store, including all the small nooks and crannies?
- They lack the proper tools/authority.

- o   Did the owners buy a cheap vacuum not meant for commercial use to save money?
- o   Do they have authority to petty-cash vacuum bags or other needed supplies to ensure they don't run out?
- They've been deprived of proper feedback.
  - o   If they've failed to meet expectations, are they told that? Or is the manager keeping a secret mental tally of every mistake they make to surprise them with a *disciplinary action* down the road?
  - o   If feedback is given, is the manager being honest or mitigating the message? An example of mitigation:
    - ▪   Mitigated: "If you could just pick up the pace a little while vacuuming, that would be great."
    - ▪   Honest: "It's taking you two hours to vacuum the store vs thirty minutes like everyone else. We need to find some way to get you closer to thirty minutes so we have time to focus on other tasks. Is there anything I can do to help you with this? I'd be happy to show you tips and tricks while vacuuming to pick up your speed."

### Dealing with Sinkers

Once I've identified a Sinker and followed the steps above to ensure we've done everything we can to set him up for success, I take the following steps:

- First Meeting
  - I explain that, from my perspective, he is not meeting expectations and something needs to change. I provide specific examples where he's fallen short.
  - I ask if he agrees with my perspective or if he has a different one. If he disagrees, we talk back and forth until we come to an alignment. If I realize my perspective was wrong and he isn't falling short of expectations, I'll react appropriately. If not, I'll continue.
  - I'll ask him if there's anything I'm doing or not doing that is holding him back, or if there is any way I can help him.
  - We decide what he and I can do going forward to fix things.
  - We come up with the consequences if things don't get better. Typically, this will be a *disciplinary action.*
  - At the end, I recap our conversation, stating clearly what we've both agreed to do and the consequences if either of us fall short of our agreed expectations. I confirm he understands and agrees.
  - We set a time (usually in two weeks, no longer than a month) to sit down and see if things have improved.
- Second Meeting
  - If things haven't improved, I apply the consequences we both agreed on in the previous meeting.
  - We have another conversation like the first about coming

up with what we both will do to make things better and the consequences if things don't improve.

- Third Meeting +
    - o I repeat the overall structure of the Second Meeting until things either get better or the consequences escalate to the point of terminating his employment.
    - o Often, the team member will end up quitting before being terminated.

## *Be Strict, Not Lenient*

Stricter managers tend to have better teams and more respect. By strict, I don't mean bogging down the team with nonsensical policies and setting them up for failure, nor do I mean be overly mean and disrespectful. By strict, I mean holding people accountable to the expectations and consequences the team has mutually agreed upon.

If everyone agrees upon the importance of arriving to work on time but one person is repeatedly late, that person should be held accountable.

If the team agrees to complete a certain task by a certain deadline but one person doesn't, that person should be held accountable.

There are a lot of ways to hold people accountable. The team should be made aware of and agree to what that means *before* being held accountable. For example, if someone doesn't complete a task by a certain deadline, unless there's a valid reason for it, should that individual get some *disciplinary action*? Should it simply be a warning for a first-time issue? Should that person be put on a Performance Improvement Plan?

Something else?

## *Collaboration*

Many managers decide where the bus is going and then find people to help drive the bus to its destination. Instead, I've found a lot more success by first finding great people and then collectively deciding where the bus should go.

I've made a lot of comments in these notes about having the team agree to the tasks, consequences, incentives, etc.

What happens if the team doesn't agree? What happens if, just to be difficult, the team refuses to agree to any consequences if they don't do their job?

What if I feel strongly that a certain aspect of the job (such as ensuring that customers leave happy) is so critical to the company's success that the consequences of failing to do so should be rather severe, but the team disagrees?

Or what if I feel that negative customer reviews or any customer complaints must be addressed within twenty-four hours, but the team feels we can wait up to a week?

A benefit of having a team of Rowers is that collectively, they can probably make better decisions than I. In *Journey to Enya*, the Rowers Martin was able to recruit in the second half of the story came up with most of the ideas that led to the voyage's success.

Whenever my team disagrees with me, either on what we should be doing or what the consequences should be, instead of trying to persuade them to agree with me, I try to understand their point of view. Maybe they have a different and better perspective than I.

If I still disagree even after understanding their point of view, I'll ask questions rather than making statements to either get them to agree with me, get me to agree with them, or get us to agree on a new option. While doing this, I'm focusing on the *interests* involved, not *positions*.

A *position* could be *I want all negative customer reviews responded to within 24 hours.*

The *interest* for that position could be *to ensure we take care of our customers quickly and appropriately.*

We typically come up with a position to achieve some interest, not just to have a position. The primary objective of a policy such as that is NOT the actual responding to the customer in twenty-four hours; it's making sure we give great customer experiences. Responding to complaints quickly is simply one method to achieve that.

If this was a conversation with my team, I would ask questions such as:

- What is your opposition to responding to negative customer reviews or complaints within twenty-four hours?
- Is this more of an issue of you not agreeing on the value in responding that quickly or you agreeing with the value but feeling it's not practical with our current resources?
- How long do you think is fair to make our unhappy customers wait for a response?
- How can we do what you're suggesting while still addressing my interest of turning all our unhappy customers into happy

ones?

- Historically, when we've responded within twenty-four hours, we've nearly always been able to turn the situation around and make the customer happy. If we change the standard to respond to unhappy customers within forty-eight hours like you're suggesting and notice we're unable to fix their problems as effectively, will you agree to switch it back to twenty-four hours?

Of course, on rare occasions, I may be unable to get my team to fully embrace something I deem important. Running everything through a majority vote is not the best way to manage a business, and sometimes a manager needs to make an unpopular decision.

When this happens, I'll say something like: "Okay, I understand your perspective and concerns with responding to reviews within twenty-four hours. This is extremely important to me. I understand you don't agree with it, but I'm asking you to respect how important this is to me and follow this policy. If this ever seems impractical given your workload and resources, please communicate with me and I'll problem-solve with you so this isn't a burden. But going forward, the expectation is that we respond to all negative customer reviews and complaints within twenty-four hours."

But if I'm doing everything else right, my team should respect me enough work with me in situations like this. However, it's extremely rare that I need to do this. Maybe once a year, but typically not even that often.

## Focus on Getting It Right, Not Being Right

Put any ego aside. I'd rather get it right rather than be right. A 'my way or the highway' mentality is horrible. If anything, I'm excited when my team disagrees with me and comes up with a better solution than I proposed. That's a sign I've got a dynamite team.

For any managers reporting to me, I'm significantly more impressed if they tell me about a solution one of their team members came up with vs one they did. It's easy to come up with solutions, but it's a sign of a great leader if instead she builds a team who comes up with those solutions themselves.

### Incentives

If the most important job of managers is getting a team of Rowers, the second most important job is coming up with incentives for those Rowers.

Incentives are so important I plan on writing a future book on them, but in short, incentives drive results. What gets incentivized gets done.

Once a manager gets a team of Rowers, instead of wasting time coming up with checklists, policies, procedures, marketing strategies, etc, simply set a simple, lucrative incentive in place that gets the Rowers thinking like owners. Empower them to act, and then step out of their way.

## *Conclusion*

When it comes to managing others, I've found the best success when managers:

1. Create a team of Rowers.
2. Remove any Sinkers quickly (first by looking inward).
3. Implement a simple, effective incentive for the team.
4. Empower the team.
5. Stay out of everyone's way and offer support.

When I'm managing a team, if I'm spending time doing anything that doesn't fall into those five steps, I'm being ineffective. Sometimes, life serves me urgent and important tasks that I need to address outside of those five steps, but I stive to minimize those tasks. If I catch myself doing tasks like those, it's because I've failed at something else, and I seek to correct it as fast as possible.

By successfully building a team of Rowers, a manager will be best prepared to handle life's curveballs. Like Martin with Sibyl, there will come a time when your team faces adversity never before experienced. Martin was only able to survive due to the ideas and passion of his crew. Similarly, having a self-motivated team of Rowers will give you your best chance to overcome any adversity and reach your personal version of Enya.

# A Personal Request for You

I would really appreciate any feedback you have on this book, and it would mean a lot to me if you left a helpful review on Amazon sharing your thoughts.

My next story is one about avoiding becoming fragile. My aim is to focus on soft skills applicable both in life and business and sharing them through fun, engaging stories. If you would like to be notified of future book releases, please subscribe to my newsletter by going to www.nickleja.com.

Also - if there are any soft skills you feel are not taught in schools or that others could benefit from knowing, please let me know. I'd love to learn about new skills and distill them into fun stories everyone can read and enjoy. You can share any ideas by going to my website.

Thank you so much for reading *Journey to Enya*!

# About the Author

Nick Leja opened his first business shortly after graduating college. Since then, he has continued to open and invest in businesses and real estate across the country in a variety of industries.

He's passionate about helping others grow by sharing his knowledge from reading and personal experiences. Trying to avoid getting "stuck" with being an adult, daydreaming is one of his favorite hobbies, and writing allows him to tap into his creativity to have fun and help others.

# More by Nick Leja

Following is an excerpt from the opening pages of Nick's recently published short story: *The Dark Fairy: a story showing individuals and teams how to listen and ensure others feel understood.*

# 1

*I may disappear soon. In case I do, I want to write down everything
I know about the Dark Fairy. Hopefully this will help you. I realize you
may not be a fairy or even know what fairies are, so I'll give a brief
background of us first.*

*Before the darkness, a large community of us lived in a mystical
village. We fairies displayed the most brilliant colors, from vivid green
hair to radiant purple wings. We loved colors like dogs love attention;
colors made our world come alive. We used colors and imagery as a way
of expressing ourselves. Just like I couldn't fully explain what the color
blue looks like to you in words, we could not fully express our feelings
without the use of colors, tastes, smells, and sounds.*

*While our wings, hair, and eyes enjoyed an abundance of color, the
land around us was mostly dull greens and browns. Although we could
fly and cast a handful of spells, we could not modify nature to make it
more vibrant. At least not on our own.*

*Fortunately for us, there existed a special Dust that allowed us to
temporarily enhance our environment in ways our own magical abilities
did not allow. This Dust was found across the land, floating gently over
the ground, glittering in the air whether under the midday sun or in the
depth of night. When a fairy discovered Dust, they could use it to enrich
the land, painting the grasses in vibrant shades of green or growing
flowers that filled the air with invigorating fragrances.*

Dust provoked surges of excitement throughout the village, but it was limited for two reasons. One, the effects of Dust were temporary, so whatever we created would slowly revert to how it had been before. Two, shortly after a cluster of Dust was disturbed, the unused Dust scattered and dissolved, so it had to be used as soon as it was found. Because of this, Dust created short spurts of joy rather than anything we could depend or rely on.

Occasionally, we would discover a huge cloud of Dust that one of us couldn't use by ourselves, so we would gather our friends and family to celebrate.

We called these celebrations latías. During latías, some fairies used Dust to create exotic gardens full of brilliant hues and aromas. Others created natural streams that burbled over the ground in a soothing rhythm. Still others would dye the grass all the colors of the rainbow, shaping and cultivating it to form intricate patterns of art. Each of us had our specialty and our personal passion when it came to using Dust. One thing we all shared, however, was our love for these latías as they were a great opportunity for everyone to have fun and unwind.

One day, Caden, a curious fairy with sharp blue eyes, ivory skin, and glowing yellow wings, set out into the wilderness looking for Dust. He loved latías and wanted to find a way to make them more frequent. For years, he had worked on inventing a magic bottle he hoped would preserve Dust, allowing us to store it for later use. That afternoon, bottle in hand, he came across a clearing in the trees where the sunlight glimmered over a large cloud of Dust.

I imagine Caden's heart raced with anticipation as he popped off the cork from his magic bottle and cast a spell, causing the Dust to rush in. When the last speck of Dust entered, he quickly slipped the cork back on, set the bottle on the grass, and sat next to it, watching it intently. After about ten minutes, Caden confirmed that the Dust inside the bottle still sparkled just as brilliantly as it always had. He had done it! He had found a way to preserve Dust!

Caden could not contain his excitement. He immediately told all of us of his new invention and showed us how it worked. He crafted as many magic bottles as he could and trained us all on how to gather and preserve Dust. Over time, he became an expert in not only how to store Dust, but also how to find it.

Because of Caden, we were able to accumulate more Dust than ever, allowing us to create ever more expressive landscapes in our village, filled with exotic colors, sounds, and smells. Because we could collect and store Dust, we could use the Dust to replenish the landscape to make our changes permanent—so long as we never ran out of it.

As we accumulated more and more Dust, something changed within our village.

Before, finding and using Dust was a community event that brought us together. We would only interact with Dust once, maybe twice a month in any substantial way.

Now, as everyone became more focused on accumulating as much Dust as possible, fairies began hoarding Dust and only using it on the land around their homes, no longer wanting to share with others.

Latias became less frequent. Fairies became more protective of their Dust. Some even became territorial when two fairies stumbled upon the same cloud of wild Dust.

The fairies who accumulated the most Dust had the most striking landscapes, luscious gardens, rolling hills, intricate fountains, and masterful blends of colors. The other fairies looked at those landscapes with reverence, even more determined to collect more Dust to enhance their own.

*While our land became more colorful, everyone seemed sad, like something was missing. No one was happy anymore, and no one really knew why.*

*Caden himself seemed the most troubled of all. He used to be so eager to teach the fairies how to gather Dust, as if that brought him great fulfillment. After a while, he looked empty, like something was weighing on him. I didn't speak with him much, but occasionally, when we would make eye contact, he always looked so sad...*

*Many times, I saw him meeting with the village elders. I'm not sure what they spoke about, but those meetings would put Caden in the worst of moods. After them, he would frequently withdraw to his home and remain there for days before coming out again.*

*About a year after we started collecting Dust, Caden called the village together to discuss something. We all gathered near the village center. This was the first time we had all been gathered in months. At first, I was excited to see everyone together, but as the fairies started trickling in, I couldn't form a smile.*

*Most of the fairies moved slowly and somberly, as if they were carrying an invisible burden on their backs. Typically, when we were together, we'd be whizzing back and forth in the air as we shared exciting stories or rolling in the grass as we laughed. But on this day, everyone appeared lifeless.*

*Once we had all gathered, Caden began speaking. He started to explain that he knew why we were all unhappy and he knew how to fix it. But in the middle of his speech, a dark magical force suddenly took hold of him. His skin turned pale, his yellow wings blackened, his eyes faded, and his voice deepened and took on a raspy tone. I had never seen anything like it. I can't explain it, but a dark aura materialized around him that seemed to control his actions and even... his thoughts.*

Caden cast several seeking spells that summoned all the fairies' magic bottles to him, leaving the fairies with no more means of collecting Dust. He used that Dust to morph the ground under our village castle, a community space we used for *latías* and other events. The ground buckled and crumbled as a massive hill pushed up towards the sky, raising the castle higher so it overlooked the entire village.

"From this day forward," Caden declared in a deep, raspy tone, "no fairies are allowed to collect or use Dust. If you do, I will vanish you."

Caden, known from that point on as the Dark Fairy, took possession of the castle and made it his home. As he gained more Dust, he spawned skeletal, blackened trees that sprouted around the land like corpses clawing at the sky, slowly draining the surrounding area of water and life. The once beautiful environment around the village began to wither into a scorched landscape void of all colors and smells.

We fairies no longer experienced any joy. All our happiness was stripped away as we were forced to live upon the ashy land.

Since then, there have been several attempts to free the fairies from Caden's control, each attempt resulting in the fairies never coming home. Three of them, I witnessed myself.

Made in the USA
Monee, IL
19 March 2023

30185163R00121